Over 100 of the

D1685162

Best Inns & Pubs
in the Cotswolds, Thames Valley
& Chilterns

Compiled by:	Joanne Brannigan (Oxfordshire & N. Bucks)
	Gordon Dunkerley (Berkshire & S. Bucks)
	Stephen Jones (Gloucestershire)
Edited by:	James Lawrence
Assisted by:	Eric Lawrence
	Stephanie Richman

CONTENTS

Published by
Bracken Publishing
Bracken House, 199a Holt Road
Cromer, Norfolk NR27 9JN

ISBN 1 871614 04 X

Printed by Broadgate Printers, Aylsham, Norfolk.

July 1990

Introduction

Ask any foreign visitor what he or she likes most about England: the answer will likely include 'your pubs'. We sometimes take them for granted, but they are unique to our country and rank amongst its greatest assets. Nowhere is the very spirit of England better expressed; they are a continuing thread through our social history, representing stability and one feels that as long as they are still there, things aren't so bad.

There have been many changes in recent years, however. Many a good pub has been ruined by the introduction of intrusive gaming machines, or that mind-assaulting raucous howling which passes for music with some people. On the other hand, the standard of beer and especially food has improved beyond recognition. I know of one pub which, 15 years ago, received newspaper coverage when it added spaghetti bolognese to the menu!

The last year or so has been a particularly turbulent one for the trade. The controversial Monopolies Commission Report has caused considerable disquiet amongst tenants, many of whom are quitting in the face of huge rent increases. Business rates are crippling others and the slump in the property market has resulted in a log-jam of unsold businesses, again resulting in confusion and uncertainty. All this has obviously complicated the compilation of this guide, as in many cases a pub could not be included simply because the licensee would probably be gone by publication date or soon thereafter.

Nevertheless, we are pleased to present this first edition, which is intended to point visitors and locals alike to some of the region's better inns and pubs. Our previous publication for East Anglia (now in its second year) has been an enormous success and we intend to follow this one with a new and enlarged edition next year. Readers' comments on establishments, whether featured or not, are most helpful in this endeavour.

We hope you find the guide useful and if it should help you to discover a good inn or pub, please tell the proprietor!

James Lawrence.

Important

Please note:-

1. Dishes quoted from menus are examples only, and not necessarily available at all times.

2. Prices, where quoted, may alter during the currency of this guide.

3. Every effort is made to ensure accuracy, but inevitably circumstances change and errors and omissions may occur. Therefore the publisher cannot accept liability for any consequences arising therefrom.

4. It is not claimed that all the best inns and pubs are featured.

5. Your comments about any establishment, favourable or not, are particularly welcome. Correspondents who especially impress the editor will receive a complimentary copy of the next edition.

6. The listing of brewers' beers and lagers does not mean that their full range is necessarily available.

7. Special note to publicans: if your house is not included, please do not be offended! The area covered is very large and time limited. If you serve good food in pleasant surrounds, please write and we will visit you.

FURTHER COPIES OF THIS OR OUR EAST ANGLIA GUIDE CAN BE OBTAINED BY SENDING A CHEQUE FOR £2.95 EACH TO BRACKEN PUBLISHING, 199a HOLT ROAD, CROMER, NORFOLK NR27 9JN

GOING EAST?

Look for these in local bookshops, tourist offices and some pubs. Or make sure you have them before you go by writing to Bracken Publishing, Bracken House, 199a Holt Road, Cromer, Norfolk NR27 9JN

Enclose cheque for £2.95 per copy, to include postage and packing.

THE ROSE AND CROWN INN

Church Lane, Ratley, Nr. Banbury.   Tel: (0295 87) 636

       Location: Next to Norman church.

Credit cards: Access, Visa, Amex, Diners.

        Beers: Hook Norton, Donnington, Batemans, Morlands, Tanglefoot, Abbott, Arkells, plus one guest. Kegs - Whitbread, Flowers, plus Murphys, Guinness, and 2 ciders.

        Lagers: Heineken, Kronenbourg 1664.

Examples from menu (bar meals lunch & evening, 7 days, restaurant Fri. & Sat. evenings only): *over 40 dishes of all kinds in the bar. Seafood cocktail, homemade soups, breaded mushrooms, stuffed plaice, beef & Guinness pie, vegetable crumble, spotted dick, lemon meringue pie. Traditional Sun. lunch. Menus changed often.*

If the 42 dishes and 12 desserts (changed daily) don't whet your appetite, have a chat to Graham behind the bar about the two resident ghosts. The pub was built around 1098 and is steeped in history: the main fireplace was allegedly the hiding place of a Roundhead during the English Civil War. The poor chap was beheaded there and may very well be one of the ghosts. The historical interest is sustained by wooden beams and mullion windows, stone walls, original flagstone floors and Inglenook fireplaces. A quiet and extremely picturesque location in which to enjoy a very wide choice of good real ales and an abundance of reasonably priced food. Children welcome in the garden. Barbecue in the summer.

5

THE BUTCHER ARMS

Farnborough Village, nr Banbury,   Tel. (029 589) 615
- Location: Off A423, 4 miles north of Banbury.
- Credit cards: Access, Visa.
- Beers: Flowers, Marstons Pedigree.
- Lagers: Stella Artois, Heineken, Warsteiner (in summer).

Examples of bar meals (lunch & evening, 7 days): *homemade soups, chicken Kiev, battered cod, scampi, chilli, homemade vegetable mornays, ploughman's, salads.*
Examples of restaurant meals (lunch & evening, 7 days): *gravadlax, smoked trout, garlic mushrooms; steak au poivre, farmer's pot, beef orange, country lamb hot pot, gammon steak. Sunday carvery. Selection of sweets.*

This pretty village is an artist's dream, and there is plenty to hold the interest of any visitor; three lakes for anglers, Farnborough Hall, and an antiques shop, but the day isn't complete without a call on this lovely old village pub. Constructed from the local Horton stone, parts of it are over 300 years old. The first impression on entering is the friendly atmosphere; Daphne and Tony Polglase welcome all but have a special sympathy for 'minorities'. For example, they offer several choices for vegetarians, and even two for vegans; pensioners and children's portions are available at reduced prices, and the latter have their own corner. The food is homecooked and noted for quality. Pleasant garden. Ample parking.

THE BRASENOSE ARMS

Cropredy, Banbury.   Tel: (0295) 750244
         Location: Nr. Banbury.
   Credit cards: Visa, Access.
            Beers: Draught Bass, Draught Guinness.
          Lagers: Carling Black Label, Tennents Extra, Tennents L.A.

Examples from menus (available lunch and evening, 7 days): *Wings of fire with mint and cucumber dip, Japanese prawns with garlic dip, chicken breast with leek and stilton sauce, steaks, homemade pies, venison in red wine sauce, lamb Shrewsbury, swordfish steak, wheat & walnut casserole. Figgy pudding with brandy sauce, whole baby coconuts, double chocolate icecream gateau.*

The unusual name derives from the large brass door koncker at Brasenose collage to which the pub once belonged. A charming place, full of character: oak beams, inglenook fireplace, a collection of paintings by local artist and a separate 17th. century a la carte restaurant. Large gardens with swings and an orchard are just 100 yards from Oxford canal. Fairport Convention, one of Britains best known folk groups, holds its annual reunion here in August, during Europe's largest folk festival. The imaginative food also includes an inspired separate vegetarian menu, homemade pies and daily specials. Children welcome.

7

THE WYKHAM ARMS

Colony Lane, Sibford Gower, nr Banbury.   Tel. (029 578) 351
- Location: Village centre.
- Credit cards: Access, Visa.
- Accommodation: Planning permission granted for 8 rooms.
- Beers: Mitchell & Butler, Bass, Hook Norton, Flowers, Marstons, all hand pumped.
- Lagers: Stella Artois, Tennents Extra, Heineken.

Examples of bar meals (lunch & evening, 7 days): *fresh sardines in crab butter, curry, two plaice fillets, vegetarian chilli, beef & Guinness pie, sirloin steak, spinach & mushroom lasagne, cottage pie, chicken Kiev, cheese/cauliflower/potato bake, ploughman's, salads, jacket potatoes. Double chocolate gateau, lemon meringue pie.* Children's menu.

Examples of restaurant meals (as above): *seafood au gratin, whole lemon sole in rosemary butter, steaks, veal escalope in herb sauce, venison in red wine.*

"Come as a guest, leave as a friend" - that's the philosophy at this amiable family pub, run by John and Carol Sivyer for the last two years or so. They feel strongly that children should not be left out, but they will doubtless head for the large landscaped gardens with swings and slides (there's also an Aunt Sally pitch). Dating from 1640, the public bar is home to a magnificent inglenook, where a fire blazes in winter, and the lounge has an enclosed well at its focus - always a great talking point. Paintings for sale by a local artist are exhibited round the walls, There's pool and darts for artists of another kind. B & B planned - ask for details.

SAYE AND SELE ARMS

Broughton, nr Banbury.   Tel. (0295) 263348
      Location: On road to Shipton, from Banbury.
  Credit cards: Not accepted.
        Beers: Davenports, Wem, Greenhall Witley.
      Lagers: Continental, Labat, low alcohol draught.

Examples from menu (lunch & evening, 7 days): *steak & kidney pie, lasagne verdi, mushrooms in garlic butter, beef pies, chicken pies, quiches, battered cod, breaded plaice, scampi, chicken in cream sauce, ploughman's, sandwiches made with local baked bread. Homemade apple pie. Traditional Sunday lunch. Blackboard specials.*

The unusual name is credited to Lord and Lady Saye and Sele, owners of Broughton Castle, just a couple of minutes walk away - many visitors make their way here. Parts of the pub date back to the 13th century, and the old world charms are still in evidence (flagstone floors, oak beams, brasses), though standards of comfort are right up to date with new upholstered seating. It enjoys a particular reputation for good homecooked food, sweet and savoury pastry dishes being a speciality. The non smoking dining room seats about 35, and parties up to 40 can be catered for. The gardens, surrounded by lovely woodland, boast an aviary with some colourful and exotic birds - children will love it, and proprietors Audrey and Frank Whittle (L.H.I.C.M.A.) welcome them inside, too. Large car park.

Oxfordshire

THE BARLEY MOW

Somerton Road, Upper Heyford.   Tel. (0869) 232300
   Location: Main street, short walk from canal.
   Credit cards: Not accepted.
   Beers: Harvest, John Bull, Tetley, plus Guinness & cider.
   Lagers: Lowenbrau, Castlemaine, Skol

Examples of bar meals (lunch & evening, 7 days): *lasagne with salad & garlic bread, chilli with rice & crusty bread, roast chicken, jacket potatoes with assorted fillings, scampi, sausages, ham & egg, assortment of fresh cut sandwiches on crusty bread.*
Examples of restaurant meals (as above): *T-bone, rump, sirloin & fillet steaks, 'He-man's' grill (lamb chop, steak, gammon, kidney, liver, mushrooms, tomato, chips & salad - £6.95), salads, basket meals.*

Cheerful and friendly service is the watchword as this small Cotswold stone pub, run by Norma and John Fellows. Their homecooked food is priced so as not to frighten your wallet, and there is suffecient diversity to cater for all tastes. One may savour it either in the bar or separate dining area, in traditional country pub surrounds. Children are welcome, but they will inevitably be drawn to the pet rabbits, guinea pigs, goat etc, and there's a large garden to soak up their exuberance. Combine your visit to this pleasant part of the county with a stroll by the nearby canal. Large car park to rear of pub.

THE TALLY HO INN

Ploughley Road, Arncott, nr Bicester.　　　　　　　Tel. (0869) 247170
　　　　　Location:　Between M40 & A41.
　　Credit cards:　Access.
Accommodation:　4 twins.
　　　　　　Beers:　Courage Best, Directors, John Smiths.
　　　　　Lagers:　Kronenbourg, Fosters, Millers.

The Tally Ho Inn CPriate 1990

Examples from bar menu (available lunch & evening, 7 days): *Huntsman lunch, homemade pies, chilli, lasagne, moussaka, jacket potatoes, fresh cut sandwiches.*
Examples from restaurant menu (available as above): *oriental prawns with choice of dips, duck with peaches & port sauce, lemon sole, hunter's pie (beef & venison in red wine), mixed grill, steaks & grills, vegetarian dishes.*

Built in 1782, with beamed ceilings and open fires, The Tally Ho is an absolute must for families. Whilst the 'oldies' indulge in good food and drink, their progeny can have the time of their lives. There's a separate room for them and a children's garden with swings, see saws and a Herbie tree, plus a zoo with goats, a pony, lambs, rabbits and an aviary. Families are also welcome in the separate 'Hunters' restaurant, where there's a good choice, including vegetarian. Barbecues on the patio in the garden, weather permitting.

THE PLOUGH INN FREEHOUSE

Merton, nr Bicester.   Tel. (086 733) 320

Location:	Merton village, between Ambrosden & Charlton-on-Otmoor.
Credit cards:	Not accepted.
Beers:	Flowers, Whitbread, Welsh keg.
Lagers:	Stella Artois, Heineken, Swann Light. Plus range of foreign bottled beers.

Examples of bar meals (lunch Mon. - Sat. and every evening): *steak & ale pie, cottage pie, chicken ham & mushroom pie, steak & kidney pie, curries, steak, lasagne, seafood platter, scampi, burgers, ploughman's, jacket potatoes, spinach & mushroom lasagne, mushroom & nut fettuccine. Apricot crumble, chocolate fudge cake, spotted dick.*

Arguably the most important thing for a public house is that it should feel homely and inviting. That's certainly true of The Plough, where proprietors Steve and Chris Sharp hold that nothing is too much trouble as far as their customers are concerned. Their handsome property was built around 1650, and has been much extended over the years. It is obviously well looked after; the polished stone, original exposed beams and inglenook fireplace are in pristine condition. One may eat in an extended dining room, and there's a function room with bar - full catering service laid on, and live entertainment on special occasions. The large beer garden is mainly laid to lawn with an Aunt Sally pitch, swings and climbing frame, and ornamental fish pond. Naturally, children are welcome.

THE OXFORD ARMS

Troy Lane, Kirtlington.   Tel. (0869) 50208
      Location: On main road in village.
Credit cards: Not accepted.
      Beers: Tetley, Harvest, John Bull.
     Lagers: Lowenbrau, Castlemaine, Skol.

Examples of bar meals (lunch & evening, 7 days): *smoked trout with horseradish, pork chop cordon bleu, chicken chasseur, vegetable & traditional lasagne, vegetable chilli, salads, ploughman's, sandwiches. Daily specials.*
Examples of restaurant meals (as above): *frogs legs in garlic butter, deep fried camembert, grilled or poached salmon, grilled tuna with caviar butter, pies, steaks, guinea fowl, half roast duckling, daily specials. Trad. Sun. lunch.*

The Oxford Arms makes its recorded debut in 1853, appearing in Lascelles Oxfordshire directory with one Thomas Rogers at the helm, who developed a parallel career as a pig dealer. It was renovated in the 60's, without destruction of the 'old world' charm, and a public bar created in a suitably modified garage - pub games are played here, and children are welcome. The restaurant was once an old fashioned parlour with beer barrels on racks and trestles, and the Polo Room came with flagstoned floor and sawdust carpeting. Connections with the sport remain strong to this day, and this is a favourite haunt of players. The menu runs to several pages, so there is something for everyone, and one may also eat in the very pleasant beer garden.

13

THE BEN JONSON

Weston on the Green.   Tel. (0869) 50320
      Location: On A43 Northampton road from Oxford.
  Credit cards: Not Accepted.
        Beers: All Halls, Burton, Harvest, Drum mild.
      Lagers: Castlemaine, Skol.

Examples from menus (lunch & evening, 7 days): *garlic mushrooms in wine and cheese sauce, chilli, lasagne, chicken with white wine cheese & tarragon, sweet & sour chicken, venison with port & mushroom sauce, ploughman's. Death by chocolate, lemon cream pie, cherry tart, apple crumble.*

When the author and friend of Will Shakespeare stayed here, the landlord promptly changed its name in his honour (it was formerly known as The Chequers). Built in 1636, it retains some of the original beams made from ships' timbers, and is altogether a very friendly traditional thatched pub. Open all day except Sundays, you can even have a full English breakfast for the ridiculous price of £2.50. Customers often have hampers prepared for them to take to Ascot or Henley. Proprietors Mr and Mrs Walker are also particularly helpful in providing small portions for children, even tiny tots can be catered for with teaplate sized helpings. A huge garden, supplied with bats and balls, gives youngsters plenty of space to run around in. Traditional pub games inside, and dogs allowed in public bar.

THE RED LION

Cattle Market, Chipping Norton.   Tel. (0608) 644641

Location: 18 miles NW of Oxford.
Credit cards: Not accepted.
Beers: Hookey, Flowers, Guinness.
Lagers: Heineken, plus Scrumpy Jack cider.

Examples from blackboard menu (lunch & evening, 7 days): *homemade soups, curries, ham & eggs, chicken, icecream & fruits.*

The only pub in town with a garden, and just a minute's walk from the centre. Proprietor Kenneth House is understandably proud of the pretty walled garden, recently completed, with seating and separate children's play area. Barbecues are held here in summer. Inside is traditionally furnished, with plenty of pub games for the competetive, though the atmosphere is always friendly. Occasional live entertainment in the shape of country or folk music adds to the fun. A good drinking pub, not 'taken over' by food (but chip fans will love it!), and open from 10:30am to 11pm except Wednesdays and Saturdays, when normal hours apply. Ample parking.

THE FALKLAND ARMS

Great Tew, nr Chipping Norton.   Tel. (060 883) 653
        Location: Off B4022 5 miles east of Chipping Norton, on village green.
    Credit cards: Not accepted.
  Accommodation: 4 doubles, one with four-poster. From £36.
           Beers: Hook Norton, Donnington, Wadworth, Halls Woodhouse.
          Lagers: Tuborg.

Examples of bar meals (12 - 2pm, Tues. - Sat. only): *mushrooms in stilton & cider, homemade soups (eg seafood, stilton & cauliflower, carrot & mint, lettuce & courgette, cheese & ale), sandwiches, lamb & leek pie, Lancashire hotpot, pork & stilton pie, homemade fishcakes, homemade faggots, pork in mushroom sauce, spicy stuffed marrow, rabbit stew, Scotch eggs. Also free range duck or chicken eggs for breakfast.*

It makes a marvellous front cover; probably one of Britain's prettiest village pubs-the classic English country inn, the kind that brings tears of wistful nostalgia to the eyes of ex-patriots. The village, too, is a little piece of Old England, having been left untouched by a benevolent, if eccentric, lord of the manor. Mellow honey-stone thatched cottages cluster round the village green, the pub being the gem amongst them. Inside lives up to expectations: well worn stone-flag floors, a magnificent inglenook, high-back settles, oak panels and beams, and a ceiling bedecked with a collection of old beer and cider mugs. Another timeless tradition, rarely observed elsewhere, is the sale of clay pipes, filled ready to smoke, and there are also about 50 snuffs from which to choose.

An outstanding choice of quality ales is dispensed from china handpumps, and country wines and ciders are also stocked, and hot punch in winter. The homecooking is wholesome, imaginative yet, again, very English and traditional. The cottagey bedrooms, one with four poster, are much in demand, so best book early. The enthusiastic comments in the visitors' book are perhaps more eloquent than the major guides and other publications in which the inn regularly features, though they all give 'rave reviews'. Sitting on the terrace amongst the roses on a summer day, drinking in the rural peace, is a relaxing and rather special experience. If you have had the foresight to reserve a room, you can also enjoy a good breakfast (eggs are from the pub's own ducks and chickens), and then explore the glorious counryside. Incidentally, the estate once belonged to that Lord Falkland after whom those islands were named.

The Falklands Arms, Great Tew.

THE WHITE HOUSE

Grove Rd. Bladon, Nr. Woodstock.
       Location: Village centre.
   Credit cards: Access, Visa.
       Beers: Burtons plus guest.
      Lagers: Lowenbrau, Skol.

Tel: (0993) 811582

Examples from menus (available lunch and evening 7 days): *three fish specials, mixed salads, homemade soup, pate, honeyroast ham, gammon & sirloin steaks, scampi, 6 types of ploughman's, homemade apple pie, treacle tart, cheesecake.*

The White House, built in the 1600's, is well used to coach loads of travellers coming to visit the resting place of Sir Winston Churchill, Blenheim Park and the churchyard, burial place of all the Churchill family. A very large montage, a tribute to Sir Winston, hangs inside on the wall, as do many pictures of the area. Leslie Evans, proprietor, takes pride in offering only traditionally brewed beer and the biggest gammon steak in town! The Olde Worlde interior has a centre servery and a separate dining area, where children are welcome. Large coach and car park. Garden with kiddies play area, Booking recommended, especially during the summer months. Party menus available.

MASONS ARMS INN

North Leigh, nr Witney.   Tel. (0993) 882005
    Location: A4095, north of Witney.
    Credit cards: Access.
    Accommodation: One family room, two twins, one double.
    Beers: Wadworth, Hook Norton, Yorkshire bitter, Toby, Mitchell &
             Butler, Beamish, Guinness.
    Lagers: Fosters, Carling, Kronenbourg.

Examples of bar meals (lunch & evening, 7 days): *cottage pie, curries, lasagne, spaghetti bolognese, salads, jacket potatoes, sandwiches, all day breakfasts.*
Examples of restaurant meals (7 – 10.30 pm, 7 days): *steaks garni, chicken Kiev, beef Bourgignon, pork in cider, lamb ragout.*

Being 450 years old, there is naturally a ghostly reputation – perhaps the undeparted is still waiting for his shoes to be repaired, as this was once a cobbler's shop! It was also once a workhouse, but is now very much a place of leisure and sport. There's a separate games room (children welcome), and teams for pool, ladies and gents darts, dominoes, Aunt Sally and quizzes. It's also HQ for North Leigh football team and on a shelf is a proud display of trophies. Further diversion is live music on Saturdays. Although a solid village local, this is not a 'cliquey' pub, and Matt and Pauline Kearney present good homemade food, a wide range of ales and a warm welcome to all. Good place to stay, with easy access to Warwick, Stratford, Oxford and Cotswolds.

THE RED LION

High Street, Bloxham, nr Banbury.   Tel. (0295) 720352
        Location: Village centre, on A361.
    Credit cards: Access, Visa.
           Beers: Wadworth 6X, IPA, Adnams Southwold. Beamish stout.
          Lagers: Heineken, Stella Artois.

Examples of bar meals (lunch & evening, 7 days): *¼lb burger, ravioli au gratin, pizza, scampi, cod, plaice, whole lemon sole, grilled local trout, gammon, sirloin steak, cold homecooked meats, ploughman's, sandwiches. Homemade weekday specials eg vegetarian, pies, pastas. Sunday roasts.*

Prices are so reasonable, you could afford to eat here several times per week! So say Paul and Carol Cooper, but the portions are generous, so while your wallet would not suffer, your waistline might. It is the sort of pub that will entice you back; a busy, friendly place that is the hub of this village on the very edge of The Cotswolds, easily accessible from Stratford and Stow. Locals like it, but there is also considerable passing trade to keep the atmosphere lively. Open fires add to the general amiability in winter. Children are welcome inside if dining with parents, but there is a large beer garden. Car parking.

THE BELL AT ADDERBURY

High Street, Adderbury, nr Banbury.   Tel. (0295) 810338
      Location: Village centre, just off main road, past village green.
Credit cards: Access, Visa, Amex.
       Beers: Hook Norton, guests.
      Lagers: Stella Artois, Heineken.

Examples of bar meals (lunch & evening, 7 days): *steak & kidney pie, liver & bacon, devilled kidneys, lamb chops, tandoori chicken, ploughman's, sandwiches.*
Examples of restaurant meals (as above): *baby edam stuffed with seafood cocktail & baked with brandy & dill, homemade merguez sausage garnished with cucumber & onion pickle; mignons of fillet steak panfried in garlic & butter & served with red onion sauce, breast of duck stuffed with foie gras chargrilled over vines & served with light apricot sauce, Dover sole grilled with butter & lemon & served with white wine & parsley sauce.*

There are records of previous landlords going back to its origins in 1783. It is unlikely any of them could have offered the kind of quality to be found here now in Le Chabrol restaurant at The Bell. The Holt family have been in charge for a year or two; the son is a qualified resident chef, the daughter looks after front of house. The menu is revised fortnightly, and for extra stimulation there are special evenings, like Vietnamese, Thai, Indian, beaujolais, but it is the French cuisine that is particularly noted. Simpler but wholesome fare is served in the two bars, or in the garden with picnic tables, but the greeting is as warm if you just call by for a drink. Children welcome.

THE LAMB & FLAG

Hailey, Witney.   Tel. (0993) 702849
    Location: Village centre.
    Credit cards: Not accepted.
    Beers: Simonds, Courage Best.
    Lagers: Fosters, Kronenbourg, Hofmeister.

Examples of bar/restaurant meals (lunch & evening, 7 days): *garlic mushrooms, prawn cocktail, seafood platter, scampi, Brian's steak & kidney pie, chicken Kiev, steaks, jacket potatoes, ploughman's, doorstep sandwiches. Trad. Sun. lunch if booked in advance. Bread pudding, cheesecake. Children's menu.*

Brian and Sue Burton are enthusiastic publicans, who run this personally as the ideal family pub, with large garden, children's amusements and Aunt Sally pitch. Brian is a qualified chef and takes care of the kitchen, and the fruits of his labour may be enjoyed in the bar or cosy dining area. Character is not lacking in this traditional Cotswold stone building; the flagstone floors are original, as well as the oak beams and settles, and the superb inglenook where fires are set in winter. Billiards and darts are played in the public bar. Large car park.

THE GRIFFIN INN

Newland Witney.   Tel: (0993) 702419
>   Location: On old A40, through the centre of Witney.
> Credit cards: Not accepted.
>   Beers: Wadworths 6X, Adnams best bitter, Toby.
>   Lagers: Stella Artois, Heineken.

Examples from menu: (lunch and evening, 7 days): *Homemade Faggott (150 year old recipe!), steak & kidney pie, chilli pork spare ribs, chilli con carne, ice cream, spotted Dick, strawberry sponge.*

Built in the 1700's, the Griffin Inn was originally an old coaching inn. With the advent of steam engines, the stream nearby was used for filling water in the old traction engines, so continued to be a popular stopping place. Recently completely refurbished, but still maintaining a very traditional feel, with two original old brewery mirrors displayed on the walls. Large beer garden with swings for the kiddies and an Aunt Sally pitch. Blackboard menu changed daily. Open all day Saturday. 100 yards from Cogges Manor Farm Museum, and well worth a visit.

THE BELL INN

Oxford Road, Enstone.   Tel: (0608) 677362
    Location: Between Woodstock and Chipping Norton, on A34.
   Credit cards: Not accepted.
      Beers: Harvest, John Bull.
     Lagers: Skol, Lowenbrau.

Examples of bar meals (available 11:30-2:30 daily): *King sized Yorkshire pudding with variety of fillings,, filled jacket potatoes, Cotswold pastie, homemade cottage pie, lasagne verdi, macaroni cheese, curry, chilli. Spotted dick with custard, chocolate sponge with sauce.*

Bill and Sue Simpson have made a name for themselves with their 'Grandma Batty's Kingsized Yorkshire puddings'. These unusual but wonderfully tasty puddings are available with no less than 12 different fillings and are exceptionally good value for money. The traditional English food is matched by a traditional Aunt Sally game in the beer garden: an original Oxfordshire game where sticks are thrown at an Aunt Sally head, or doll. Partly clad in Cotswold stone, horse brasses on the walls, original wooden beams and open fires in winter. Raffle every Sunday with 10 joints of meat to be won.

THE BELL

Sheep Street, Bicester.   Tel. (0869) 252220

           Location: Town centre.
    Credit cards: Access, Visa.
              Beers: Ruddles, Websters.
             Lagers: Budweiser, Fosters, Carlsberg, Holsten, Kaliber.

Examples from menu (lunch & evening, 7 days): *pizzas (speciality), deep fried camembert, tuna pate, lamb cacciatore, vegetable lasagne, breast of chicken with stilton sauce, beef & peppercorn casserole, pasta & tuna salad. Paris breast (choux pastry with chocolate, cream & fruit), Mississippi mud pie, profiteroles.*

All true pizza fans should beat a path to The Bell - it won Britain's first 'Pizza Pub of the Year' competition. 14 different toppings are served in a separate air conditioned pizzeria and bistro area, but start perhaps with a homemade soup, and accompany with a fresh and very different salad. The restaurant is also Italian style, but the pub itself is traditional English - beams, stone walls, lots of paintings (some humourous). An open fire warms in winter, and one may eat and drink on the patio in summer; the garden has plenty of seating and an outside bar. Certainly a pub with a difference, and not one to be missed. Children welcome.

THE MASONS ARMS

Shipton Road, Fulbrook, nr. Burford.   Tel: (0993) 822354

     Location: 1 1/2 miles out of Burford, On Chipping Norton road.
Credit cards: Not accepted.
        Beers: Wadworth 6X, Hook Norton best bitter, Flowers best bitter,
               Beamish Irish stout.
       Lagers: Kronenbourg.

Examples from menu (lunch and evening, 7 days). *6 different pies including: Steak &
kidney, boozy beef, and lamb and apricot, chicken quarters, Bibury trout, gammon steak
and egg, hot jumbo sausage in roll, fruit crumbles, syrup sponge, fresh fruit salad.*

An affectionate and comfortable pub, overlooking Fulbrook's Norman church, that
welcomes locals and visitors with equal enthusiasm. Originally 3 cottages built over
300 years ago, it has served as a pub for some 200 years, retaining original beams
and built in typical Cotswold stone. The large central fireplace is a hospitable
feature in the winter, whilst summer patrons can stretch out in the sun in the pretty,
secluded patio garden. (Barbecues ocasionally too!). Blackboard menu with daily
specials, including soups and puddings. Children welcome.

THE THATCHED TAVERN

Eaton Road, Appleton.   Tel. (0865) 864814
          Location: ¹/₂ mile off A420, 4 miles west of Oxford.
     Credit cards: Not accepted.
            Beers: Ansells Best, Tetleys.
           Lagers: Lowenbrau, Castlemaine XXXX, Skol.

Examples from menu (lunch & evening, 7 days): *surf & turf, 1lb Oxford champion sausage with egg & chips, wicked whopper mixed grill, homemade chilli, homemade curry, pork steak Chinese style, grilled trout, scampi, lasagne, chicken Kiev, steaks, ploughman's, sandwiches.*

Curiously without thatch, and with no trace in the records of when it was thatched, this could be a challenge to inquisitive sleuths, perhaps. Originally three or four cottages, believed to have been built in the 13th century, this is a very pretty village pub, with stone walls, low beamed ceilings and two open log fires. It was also the original home of the famous Appleton Bellringers. 'Aunt Sally' and darts are played on a league basis. However, it is the food that draws most custom; imaginative and in generous portions, and children welcome to partake. Parties up to 24 catered for. Car park.

THE MAYTIME

Asthall, nr Burford.   Tel. (0993 82) 2068

        Location: Village centre, near church.
    Credit cards: Access, Visa, Amex.
   Accommodation: 2 doubles, 4 twins, with private facilities. From £35 single
                   £48 double.
           Beers: Wadworth 6X, John Smith's, Tartan.
          Lagers: Stella Artois, Castlemaine XXXX.

Examples of bar meals (lunch & evening, 7 days): *steak & kidney tray (in red wine sauce), seafood tray, special Maytime pastry dishes, chicken & mushroom tagliatelli, curries, omelettes, ploughman's, steak. Burford sherry trifle, granny's treacle tart & custard.*
Examples of restaurant meals (available as above): *Maytime rich pate, Cotswold style mushrooms; lemon sole Morgan style, escalope of veal Witney, Maytime fillet steak, Burford lamb cutlet, giant prawns, vegetable pancakes. Trad. Sun lunch (£6.95).*

Now one of the most popular and lively inns in the area, some of the regulars will remember when this lovely 16th century traditional Cotswold hostelry was run down and condemned. That was back in 1975, when Tim and Mary Morgan bought it and began the transformation, establishing a reputation for warm hospitality and good food at sensible prices. They offer an "instant business lunch", prepared in minutes for those in a hurry, and children and other pets are welcome - a children's menu is available in the restaurant. This is a superb base for touring, with the recent addition of very comfortable bedrooms, and is also an excellent venue for weddings or private dinner parties. Rated highly by most major guides.

THE FARMERS

Sheep Street, Charlbury.　　　　　　　　　　　　　　　Tel. (0608) 810780

Location:	Charlbury town centre.
Credit cards:	not accepted.
Beers:	Inde Coope, Burtons Ale, Harvest Ale, Keg John Bull, Ansells.
Lagers:	Castlemaine XXXX, Lowenbrau.

Examples from lunch menu (7 days): *quiches, tuna & courgette bake, country fish pie, steak & kidney pie, gammon steak, salad, ploughman's.*
Examples from evening menu (7 days): *breast of chicken with broccoli and cream cheese, nutty mushroom and Stilton pie, vegetable stroganoff, lasagne, sirloin steak with mushrooms, country fish pie in puff pastry. Chocolate mint ice meringue, blackcurrant cheesecake, coffee and walnut gateau.*

Certainly plenty of entertainment on offer here! Traditional pub games such as darts, dominoes and an Aunt Sally pitch, and on Tuesday evenings a general knowledge quiz with a gallon of beer for the winners. Stone walls, oak beams and inglenook fireplaces – one housing an original Victorian stove – make the homely atmosphere, and the intriguing split-level restaurant is decorated with old farming memorabilia. The proprietors, both ex-farmers, take pride in their home-cooked food all reasonably priced, and also their real ales, being a Member of the Guild of Master Cellarmen. Children welcome. Car parking.

THE ROSE & CROWN

North Parade Avenue, Oxford.   Tel. (0865) 510551
    Location: Central north Oxford. 2nd left on Banbury road, after leaving
              St Giles.
Credit cards: Not accepted.
      Beers: Halls Harvest, Ind Coope Burton, Wadworth 6X.
     Lagers: Lowenbrau, Skol. Plus Guinness & Gaymers Olde English cider.

Examples from lunch menu (12 - 2:15pm, Mon. - Sat.)· *homemade hot dish of the day,*
'ploughpeoples' lunch, filled crispy baked potatoes, salads, omelettes, sandwiches.
Sunday lunch (12 - 2:15pm): *3 roasts, traditional or in giant sandwich with salad, or*
any dish from supper menu.
Examples from supper menu (7 - 8:45pm, 7 days plus Sun. lunch): *Arabian beef &*
raisin Kibbeh, green pepper & red bean lasagne (veg.), smoked haddock crumble, dish of
day. Lunch barbecues in summer (weather permitting).

An old fashioned pub with wooden tables and chairs, the Rose & Crown is located
in a narrow one-way street, grandly known as an avenue, amid an interesting array
of shops, restaurants and wine bar. The atmosphere is traditional, unspoiled by
intrusive juke box or fruit machines. Popular with 'town' and 'gown' alike, it is used
by many interesting local characters. Other than conversation, the only sound is
that of the pub piano most Tuesdays from 9pm. In the absence of more usual pub
games, regulars form teams for anything from cricket to 'dongola racing', quizzes,
and even ice hockey. Though warm and welcoming, the pub is not really suitable
for children. Recommended by major guides.

THE KINGS ARMS

Church Road, Sandford on Thames.   Tel. (0865) 777095
  Location: Through village, alongside Thames at Sandford Lock.
  Credit cards: Access, Visa.
    Beers: Courage Best, Directors, John Smiths.
    Lagers: Fosters, Kronenbourg, LA.

Examples of bar meals (cold food from 12 - 9pm in summer, hot meals lunch & evening, 7 days): *steaks, fish specials, daily vegetarian dish, chargrilled smoked duck or chicken or rack of lamb (specialities - smoked on premises), homemade pies, lasagne, stroganoff, moussaka. Desserts from cold cabinet. Children's menu.*

Originally a paper mill, The King's Arms occupies a marvellous position on the towpath beside the river Thames, and ofcourse is popular with boating folk who can moor alongside. Built in the 15th century from oak timbers, its open plan interior is split into snug areas on different levels, full of old style furniture, and bedecked with a collection of old prints. Open fires cast a warm glow in winter, but in summer the barbecue is lit in the large beer garden, which also has children's play equipment. The fragrance of steaks sizzling in full view on the griddle in the evenings is hard to resist, and few other pubs can boast a smokehouse. Open 11am to 11pm in summer, but closed from 3pm to 6pm in winter. Look out for monthly live entertainment nights - jazz, perhaps.

THE KILLINGWORTH CASTLE

Glympton Road, Wootton, nr Woodstock.   Tel. (0993) 811401
Location:	Off A34 & A423.
Credit cards:	Amex.
Accommodation:	3 doubles, one single.
Beers:	Morlands.
Lagers:	Kaltenberg, Stella Artois.

Examples of bar meals (lunch & evening, 7 days): *Yorkshire puddings with choice of stuffings, homemade steak pie, lasagne, curry, steaks, chicken with barbecue sauce, deep fried plaice with prawn & mushroom sauce, scampi, Danish open sandwiches, salads, daily specials, vegetarian meals. Chocolate fudge cake, fruit crumble, homemade trifle.* Note: new 22 seater restaurant due winter '90/'91.

Visitors often comment how much they feel at home here. That special comfortable, friendly atmosphere is hard to define and eludes many a publican, but Mr and Mrs Andrew Roberts seem to make the most of their characterful 353-year-old inn. Homecooked food is always available during open hours, at very reasonable prices. A large barbecue in the garden is always an extra pleasure in summer. Various live music is performed on some Saturday afternoons, but folk music fans note that every Friday is your night for live entertainment. A function room for 60 is a most suitable venue for weddings receptions, private parties, conferences etc. Large car park. Children welcome. After a comfortable night's stay, enjoy a hearty breakfast and maybe visit nearby Blenheim Palace.

THE RED LION

South Street, Steeple Aston, nr Oxford.   Tel. (0869) 40225
Location: Edge of village.
Credit cards: Access, Visa.
Beers: Hook Norton, Wadworth, Tanglefoot, Beamish stout.
Lagers: Carlsberg, Bitburg.

Examples of bar meals (12 – 2pm, Mon. – Sat.): *soup, ploughman's, platter of smoked salmon, summer salads, winter hotpots.*
Examples of restaurant meals (7.30 – 9.15pm, Tues. – Sat.): *fish soup with rouille, peppered smoked loin of pork with palm heart; marinated venison steak with sour cream sauce, fillets of lemon sole with hollandaise sauce, roast stuffed breast of goose, sirloin steak with green peppercorn sauce. Chilled souffle of chocolate, poached pears with caramel & raspberry coulis.*

Over 18 years of continuity and high standards is a rarity in the pub trade. The Red Lion was in a state of ruin when Colin and Margaret Mead bought it in early 1972, but has now been restored with sensitivity to create just a single bar and small, exclusive dining room. Evening meals enjoy a particularly good reputation, and an extensive wine list accompanies, so booking is strongly advised. Drinkers will appreciate being able to take their pleasures separate from diners, to enjoy all the more the traditional beers, fine wines and older spirits in an atmosphere both cannily stimulating and relaxing, without the intrusion of 'wallpaper music'. Children not permitted in bar, but there's a floral terrace in summer. Limited parking.

THE WHEATSHEAF

3 The Green, Drayton, nr Abingdon.   Tel. (0235) 531485
    Location: Village centre, 8 miles south of Oxford.
Credit cards: Not accepted.
    Beers: Morlands, Revival, Guinness.
    Lagers: Kaltenberg, Heineken.

Examples of bar meals (lunch & evening, except Sun. evening.): *crispy mushrooms, cottage pie, spinach & rice cakes with tomato & herb sauce, sirloin steak, gammon & egg, ham & egg. Daily blackboard specials eg plaice stuffed with prawns & mushrooms, chicken Kiev, chilli, lasagne.*

Ed and Topsy Osbon moved here only in Feb. '90, and have great plans for development. However, you don't have to wait to enjoy the fresh, homecooked food, very original and prepared with flair (Mrs Osbon is a cordon bleu chef with 9 years experience). Their's is the archetypal village pub-on-the-green, its two bars very cosy and quaint, and with that special friendly 'local' atmosphere. It was burnt down in 1790 and rebuilt, so presumably the alleged ghost is of a time after that, but it is said (not by the Osbons) that he or she is prone to throw glasses off shelves! Children are welcome, and there's a pleasant sheltered garden with tables and seating, and an Aunt Sally pitch.

MACHINE MAN INN

Fieldside, Long Wittenham.   Tel. (086730) 7835
Location: Just off A415 from Abingdon.
Credit cards: Not accepted.
Accommodation: 2 doubles, en suite. (Tourist Board 2 crowns).
Beers: Buckleys Best, Royal Oak, Pedigree. Murphys, Guinness.
Lagers: Fosters, Labatts, Kronenbourg.

Examples from bar & restaurant menus (lunch & evening 7 days): *white fish special, chicken korma, steak in Guinness or real ale, chicken madras, grills & steaks, seasonal game dishes, Fri. & Sat. specials. Pancakes, apple & rhubarb pie, banana splits, icecreams. Traditional Sunday lunch.*

Although there are three versions explaining the origins of the unusual name, the most commonly believed is that the first landlord had a threshing machine. Go along to the pub to hear the other two. It was built in 1865, having that unmistakable Victorian feel, and is very much the traditional village pub, with open fires, oak settles etc. A collection of cricketers' autographs reflects an interest of the landlord, another being real ales - the pub is featured in the Camra guide. Close to Dorchester and the Thames in picturesque countryside. Children welcome.

THE NUT TREE

Murcott, nr Islip.   Tel. (086 733) 253
        Location: 8 miles north of Oxford on Oxford plain.
    Credit cards: Not accepted.
           Beers: Wadworth 6X, London Pride, ABC, Burton, Tetley, guest.
          Lagers: Lowenbrau, Stella Artois, Castlemaine XXXX, Swan Lite.

Examples of bar meals (lunch & evening, Mon. - Sat.): *homemade steakburger, local sausages, sandwiches, salad bar (summer) incl. various pies, daily specials eg fresh fish, curries, lasagne, chilli.*
Examples of restaurant meals (as above): *king prawns with garlic mayonnaise or hot with garlic butter, steaks, fish platter, salmon nantua (with lobster, brandy & cream sauce), scampi, chicken Kiev, gammon with curried peach, salads.*

This area was made famous by the Otmoor rioters of the 18/19th centuries, who objected violently to the Enclosure Acts. The pub was ancient even then, having been built around 1420, and stands serenely in what is now a peaceful location, with 'only' the noises of geese, ducks, peacocks, donkeys and rabbits, all kept in the grounds, to disturb the tranquility. Children will, ofcourse, love the garden with patio, but may also dine in the conservatory. Gordon and Diane Evans have built their trade by always offering good value food and beer in a welcoming atmosphere. They now take bookings for parties up to 25 (sit down) or 50 (buffet). Sunday evening is darts night (there are also dominoes).

THE RED LION

High Street, Islip.   Tel. (086 75) 5367

Location:	Village centre.
Credit cards:	Mastercard, Visa.
Beers:	Tetley, Burton.
Lagers:	Castlemaine, Skol.

Examples of bar meals (lunchtime 7 days, evenings Tues. – Sun.): *filled pitta bread, chicken satay, vegetarian rissoles, sandwiches, ploughman's, basket meals.*
Examples of restaurant meals (as above, bookings 7 – 7.30pm only): *king prawns in garlic, hot prawn platter, garlic mushrooms, steaks with choice of 10 toppings, beef with Guinness & orange in bouchee pastry case.*

This very old Cotswold stone pub was built in the grounds of Edward the Confessor's country palace. The exceptionally large garden can seat around 100 people and has a sizeable barbecue which gets crackling every Sunday lunchtime, weather permitting. Youngsters can let off steam on the swings and wooden play frame, while the relieved adults can pursue other interests – Bruce and Angela's collection of 350 beer mugs, for instance. Children over 10 are welcome in the restaurant, where steaks are the speciality, with 10 different toppings and there are always vegetarian alternatives. Two function rooms are available for small receptions, private dinners etc. Please book well in advance.

COACHMAKERS ARMS

St Mary's Street, Wallingford.   Tel. (0491) 39382
  Location: Edge of town centre.
  Credit cards: Not accepted.
  Beers: Brakspears.
  Lagers: Stella Artois, Heineken.

Examples of bar snacks (lunchtime & evening, 7 days): *scampi, lasagne, ploughman's, sandwiches, daily specials.*
Examples of restaurant meals (every evening): *chicken breast in port wine sauce, salmon & prawns en croute, chicken breast in leek & stilton sauce, trout with celery & walnut, duckling à l'orange. Hot chocolate fudge cake, icecreams, fruit sundae. Trad. Sun. roasts at lunchtime.*

Probably the oldest in Wallingford, this 16th century timbered pub was once known as The Ramping Cat, as a landlady of 100 years ago bred felines that would stroll nonchalantly around. Today, the large through bar still has cats, but in the form of a collection of prints and ornaments. Philip and Kim Bray have been here three years or so, and are investigating the history whilst adding to this collection. The cottagey dining room (children welcome) is in pine and filled with dried flower arrangements - a charming venue for Sunday lunch, but as this is currently the only pub in town that does roasts, it's wise to book. A guitar vocalist entertains on Friday evenings. To the rear, a delightful enclosed garden has tables and chairs.

THE CHEQUERS

Berrick Salome, nr Wallingford.   Tel. (0865) 891279
Location: Off B4009, near Benson.
Credit cards: Pending.
Beers: Brakspears. Plus Guinness & cider.
Lagers: Stella Artois, Heineken.

Examples of bar meals (lunch & evening except Mon. lunch, when pub is closed):
*Simon's prawn cocktail (gigantic), Cumberland sausages, steak & kidney in red wine,
chicken cheese & tarragon, Somerset casserole (vegetarian), melange Bourgignon (veg.),
ploughman's platter, various lasagnes, steaks, gammon, sandwiches, salads.*
Examples of restaurant meals (as above): *pork in brandy and black cherries, steaks,
half roast chicken, scampi, plaice fillet, vegetarian, some dishes as above.*

It's good to know there are still places where you can get a good three course meal
for £10 or even less - but then the new landlord claims to be 'mad', anyway! His pub
straddles the boundary between two parishes, with a little stream running past the
door, and is of uncertain age, its origins lost to antiquity. Certainly it is a newcomer
compared to the tiny 11th century church nearby, and has been a post office in its
time. What is now the restaurant once once a granary, hence the lofty 40' ceiling,
and one may eat here or in the timbered lounge or small bar with open fires - there
are no strict rules about this; informality is encouraged. Children are welcome and
have half an acre of garden in which to romp. Ample parking.

SEVEN STARS

Marsh Baldon, nr Nuneham Courtney. Tel. (086 738) 255
Location: Edge of village green.
Credit cards: Not accepted.
Beers: Ushers Best, Ruddles County, Websters. Regular guest ales.
Lagers: Good range of lagers & ciders.

Examples of bar meals (lunch & evening, 7 days): *Baldon fidget pie, chicken en croute, lamb & apricot pie, feuillete of prawns & stilton, salad bar, quiches, vegetarian dishes, cold meats & pies.*

Good food and real ales are obviously a source of great pleasure to proprietors Richard and Jan Savage. All food is homemade, including the chips, and they even use their own free range eggs. They also run some inspired 'foods from around the world' evenings, with dishes from Germany, Poland, Arabia (look out for Arabic maps and memorabilia), and many others. To further 'fire' your interest there is an amazing collection of matchboxes: between 700 and 800, in fact! The garden is large with plenty of seating and an Aunt Sally pitch, and is shared with the hens, wandering freely. Cricket is played at weekends on the adjacent village green, said to be the largest in Europe. An attractive, rural location yet less than 5 miles from the centre of Oxford. Caravan club site at rear of pub.

THE BEAR & RAGGED STAFF FREEHOUSE

Bear lane, Stadhampton.   Tel. (0865) 890714
            Location: Towards Wallingford from Oxford & junction 7 M40.
        Credit cards: Access, Visa, Amex, Connect.
               Beers: Flowers, Whitbreads Best, Murphys.
              Lagers: Stella Artois, Heineken.

Examples from menus (lunch 7 days, evening Tues. - Sat.): *guacamole dip, beef &
chilli tacos, chilli 'el bear', cajun chicken, spaghetti carbonara, peppered sirloin, curry,
stuffed plaice, haddock, scampi, chicken Kiev, jacket potatoes, doorstep sandwiches.*

A very pretty 16th century stone building, apparently somewhat haunted! A figure
has been spotted, and Scottish proprietors, Liz and Mark Alexander, are trying to
find out who he is (or was) that is switching off lights and knocking glasses off
shelves. They have been in catering since leaving school, and offer a most unusual
and varied menu, Mexican food being the speciality, not available elsewhere in
these parts. They also specialise in 'doorstep' sandwiches and filled jacket potatoes,
and barbecues are good fun in the massive garden in summer. Indoor entertainment
comes in the shape of darts, dominoes, shut-the-box and satellite TV! Coach tours
accepted, and children. Large car park. Accommodation planned for mid 1991.
Here's a challenge - eat a spaghetti bolognese and get seconds free!

THE SIX BELLS

44 Lower High Street, Thame.　　　　　　　　　　　Tel. (0844 21) 2088

Location:	Edge of town, on Oxford Road.
Credit cards:	Access, Visa, Mastercard, Eurocard.
Beers:	Cask conditioned Harvest, Tetley, John Bull keg.
Lagers:	Lowenbrau, Castlemaine, Skol.

Examples of bar snacks (lunch Mon. - Sat., evening Tues. - Sat.): *rump steak, lasagne verdi, chilli, scampi, 2 smoked mackerel fillets, brunch, omelettes, ploughman's, sandwiches/rolls, daily specials.*

Examples of restaurant meals (lunch & evening, Tues. - Sat.): *bon holm herring, savoury mushrooms on toast; steaks, escalope of veal boursin, river trout meuniere, chicken Kiev, grilled noisettes of lamb with redcurrant jelly. White peaches in brandy, fruit pie, chocolate fudge cake.*

"The first pub in, and last out", as the saying goes. Whether you're coming or going, it's worth calling here at the edge of town on the way to Oxford. Its building (using old ships' timbers) in 1505 coincided conveniently with the completion of the nearby church, started 200 years or so before, and the bells of which give the pub its name. The river Thame is just 200 yds away, and a famous pop star lives very near. You may hear his songs piped softly in the lounge or restaurant bar, but there are no electronic games to disrupt the relaxed family atmosphere, fostered by Philip and Ruth Hale over the last two years. Children will love the barbecues, held on fine weekends in the enclosed patio with seating for 50. One of the few pubs in town with a car park.

THE FARMER INN

Stoke Row, nr Henley-on-Thames.   Tel. (0491) 680379

         Location: Village centre.
      Credit cards: Not accepted.
            Beers: Morlands, Brakspears, Flowers.
           Lagers: Kaltenberg, Stella Artois, Heineken..

Examples of bar meals (lunch & evenings, except Sun. evening): *homemade soup, deep fried mushrooms, 8ozs rump steak, salmon steak, curries, homecooked ham, vegetarian dishes, daily specials. Good selection of homemade puddings. Trad. Sun. roasts.*

The village is famous for its 'Maharajah's Well' - sounds unlikely in the quiet wooded countryside of south Oxfordshire, but ask Alan at The Farmer for the background story. His pub has been tastefully refurnished with polished mahogany tables and velvet upholstered seating. The L-shaped bar has its full complement of oak beams, and stripped brick walls and open fireplace with log burner. Pictures of old Stoke Row adorn the panelled walls. In addition, there's a quiet lounge and 'Farmers Kitchen' with servery, and no awful juke boxes or intrusive gaming machines to shatter the peace and enjoyment of good food. Children are welcome, and there's a patio. Good parking.

THE TRAVELLERS WELCOME

8 Main Road, East Hagbourne, nr Didcot.   Tel. (0235) 812391
Location: Village centre.
Credit cards: Access, Visa, Mastercard, Eurocard.
Beers: Ruddles, Websters.
Lagers: Carlsberg.

Examples from menu (available in bar or restaurant, lunch & evening, 7 days): *chilli, curry, giant Yorkshire puddings, scampi, breaded plaice filled with prawn & mushroom in white wine sauce, salads, jacket potatoes, steaks, half roast duck or chicken, cannelloni, macaroni cheese. Trad. Sun roast, vegetarian roast. Special pizza menu.*

East Hagbourne is a very old and pretty village, reminiscent somewhat of parts of Kent. Set amongst its thatched cottages, The Travellers Welcome has a long established reputation for hospitality and nourishing home prepared food. The selection is enormous, with pizzas something of a speciality (choose your own toppings), and a separate menu for children. Mervyn and Margaret Beesley have been here 20 years, so they are obviously doing something right! Competitive prices never deter anyone (for extra value look for special offer blackboard) and Sunday lunches are especially popular. Parties are catered for, and outside bars professionally run. Garden and large car park.

THE PACK HORSE

Woodcote Road, Chazey Heath, Mapledurham. Tel. (0734) 722140
Location: A4074, 4 miles north of Reading.
Credit cards: Not accepted.
Beers: Gales HSB & Best, Butser Brew.
Lagers: Stella Artois, Castlemaine, Carlsberg.

Examples of bar meals (lunch & evening, except Sun. evening): *steak in French bread, special pates with toast, Cornish smoked mackerel, homemade quiche, curries, chilli, salads, doubledecker toasted sandwiches, ploughman's.*
Examples of dining room meals (as above): *8ozs sirloin steak, deep-fried chicken, plaice, gammon, scampi, moussaka, beef chasseur, vegetarian, blackboard specials.*

Customers travel here from miles around, such is the good name of John Andrews' 15th century pub, converted from two cottages. He takes pride in his real ales, and stocks the full range of Gales Olde English wines. Three principal areas make up the bright and roomy interior; the dining area, with its own bar, seats 40 in wheelback chairs at polished tables; the lounge is older, timber-beamed and with pictures of old Mapledurham; this opens into the main bar, also timbered and with a large inglenook log fireplace as its finest feature. French windows lead to a magnificent garden. Children welcome. Incidentally, those who remember 'The Forsyte Saga' will know of Mapledurham House, close by.

THE ROYAL OAK

School Green, Shinfield, nr Reading.   Tel. (0734) 882931

Location:	Village centre.
Credit cards:	Not accepted.
Beers:	Morlands Bitter, Old Masters, Revival.
Lagers:	Stella Artois, Heineken, Kaltenberg.

Examples from lunchtime menu (7 days): *gammon, scampi, plaice, haddock, burgers, various salads, ploughman's, wide range of sandwiches. Trad. Sun. roasts.*
Examples of evening menu (Mon. - Sat.): *smoked mackerel, whitebait, rump steak, lasagne, Napoleon chicken, escalope of pork, gammon steak.*

Since being extended some six years ago, this has become one of the most popular pubs in the area. Besides the public bar with games area, there is a large comfortable lounge, where most food is served, though many choose to eat in the sizeable garden in kind weather. The menus are extensive and diverse, and the portions generous (children have their own menu). The fact that hosts Mick and Gill Fay are usually kept busy is eloquent testimony to good value, but they still find time to warmly welcome visitors, and the atmosphere is always lively. Children may dine with parents, or there's a play area in the garden. Large car park.

THE GEORGE & DRAGON

Church Road, Swallowfield, nr. Reading.   Tel: (0734) 884432

Location: To east of village past church and River Blackwater.
Credit cards: Not accepted.
Beers: Wethereds, Whitbread, Flowers (Summer choice), Winter Royal (in season), Guinness, Murphys.

Examples of bar meals (available lunchtimes 12-2:00): *Soups, scampi, plaice, Pizzas, curries, ploughmans, sandwitches, traditional Sunday roasts.*
(Available evenings 6:30-9:00): *House roasts (changes daily), sirloin and rump steaks, gammon steaks, cod and plaice fillets.*

A warm welcome is assured at this unpretentious country pub, converted from a farm-house during the last century. Situated in a peaceful rural area, it is hard to beleive that Reading and the busy M4 are only a few miles away. The beamed lounge is spacious and comfortable, there's a cosy snug, and the public bar has Bar Billiards and Pool tables. The old game of 'Aunt Sally' is played outside in the summer. Landlord Alan Slater takes great pride in the excellent real ales, and wife Laura takes similar pride in her wholesome and substantial meals - prices are most reasonable. In summer it is a delight to eat in the large garden overlooking the sheep grazing in the adjacent fields. Attractions in the area include Swallowfield Park with its renowned Manor House and the Wellington Country Park. Children welcome. Large car park.

THE OLD ELM TREE

Beech Hill, Nr. Reading.   Tel: (0734) 883505

Location:	Centre of village just past pond on left hand side of road.
Credit cards:	Visa, Access.
Beers:	Whitbreads, Flowers, Eldridge Pope.
Lagers:	Stella Artois, Heineken.

Examples of bar meals (available lunchtimes and evenings except Sunday evening): *Gammon steak, lasagne, seafood pancakes, sirloin steak, moules Mariniere, homemade pies, homemade pizzas, fresh fish.*

Examples of restaurant meals (available lunchtimes and evenings except Sunday evening and all day Monday): *various homemade soups, boneless roast poussin with grape stuffing & basil cream sauce, poached fillet of turbot stuffed with hazelnut mousse, fillet & sirloin steaks served with sauce or grilled to order, various game dishes in season. All cooked to order.*

Close to Berks/Hants. border, this is an idyllic location, and the view from the restaurant and lounge over the Duke of Wellington's Stratfield Saye estate is magnificent. Owners John and Janet Harrison had both worked as cabin crew for British Airways prior to takng over the Old Elm Tree just over five years ago. During this time they have brought about a remarkable transformation, and the opinions of the locals bear eloquent testimony to this. There is a large, comfortable lounge with oak beams, and the public bar has an open fireplace fuelled by logs and a separate games section linked by an archway. The restaurant is very tastefully furnished and decorated, and the food is of excellent quality and reasonably priced. Children are welcome with parents in the restaurant. Large car park.

THE HORSE & GROOM

The Street, Mortimer, Reading.   Tel. (0734) 332542

Location:	Opposite the common.
Credit cards:	Access, Visa.
Beers:	Harvest, John Bull, Burton, Ind Coope dark mild. Guinness.
Lagers:	Lowenbrau, Skol, Castlemaine XXXX.

Examples of bar meals (lunch & evening, 7 days): *variety of omelettes, beef cutlets, chicken Kiev, steaks, gammon, scampi, ploughman's with own special pickle, homemade specials, vegetarian dishes, salad bar in summer.*

Since Peter and Gail Morris took over in late 1988, The Horse & Groom has been completely transformed both in appearance and atmosphere. The saloon bar has been tastefully refurbished with velvet covered seats and polished tables, to give an air of late Victorian elegance. The spacious public bar has a pool table. The food is well prepared with quick service and at reasonable prices, and children may enjoy a meal with their parents in the lounge or in the large, beautifully kept garden. Here there is an enclosed playground, and pets corner, with pony, ducks, chickens. guinea pigs and large aviary. Situated in the Hants/Berks border, Mortimer has a long and interesting history going back to Roman times. The Roman town of Calleva is nearby, and Stratfield Saye country park.

THE BULL COUNTRY INN

Stanford Dingley, nr Reading.   Tel: (0734) 744409

Location: Centre of village, opposite green
Credit cards: Not accepted.
Beers: Charringtons, Bass, Eldridge Pope.
Lagers: Carling, Tennants extra.

Examples of bar meals (available lunchtimes, and evenings from 7pm): *Stilton soup, beef Stroganoff, turkey almond (turkey breast in mushroom yoghurt topped with almonds), chicken Provencale, drunken fish pie, good steaks (rump & sirloin).*

One of Berkshire's most beautiful villages. Stanford Dingley stands on the river Pang and has a history chronicled from the 11th century. The Bull, a 15th century coaching inn, is a freehouse owned and run by Trudi and Patrick Langdon, who take an obvious pride in it and the village. The locals gather in the public bar (which can have changed very little over the centuries, with oak beams and pillars, an open log-fuelled fire place and a section of the original 'wattle and daub' wall), and play the ancient game of 'Ring the Bull', the origins of which are lost in antiquity. There is also a nicely furnished saloon bar, somewhat quieter than the public, where Trudi and Pat are on hand with their imaginative menu of good homemade food, all at reasonable prices whether you want a 3-course meal or just a snack. Children are very welcome with parents in the saloon bar at lunchtimes and early evenings. Nicely kept gardens. Large car park.

THE BLACKBIRD

Bagnor, Nr. Newbury.   Tel: (0635) 40638

Location: Next to village green, opp. river Lambourn.
Credit cards: Visa, Access.
Beers: Ushers, Ruddles, Guinness.
Lagers: Carlsberg, Holsten, Foster.

Examples of bar meals (available lunch and evenings, except Sunday, Monday and Tuesday evenings): *steak & mushroom pie, chicken Kiev, chilli, vegetarian dishes.*
Examples of dining area meals (available lunch and evenings, except Sunday, Monday and Tuesday): *breast of duck, poached salmon, prime Scotch steaks, roast rack of lamb, fresh local trout, traditional Sunday roasts.*

There are several reason for visiting the small but attractive village of Bagnor; Donnington Castle and Snelsmore Country Park are nearby; the famous Watermill theatre; and of course the Blackbird. Comfortably furnished, its walls and beams are bedecked with china plates, bottles of all shapes and sizes, antique guns, toby jugs and many interesting pictures. At one end of the long bar is an attractively laid out dining area with open log fire. John and Sally Newbrook are friendly hosts, justly proud of a reputation for fine food. All is home cooked, the portions generous and the prices reasonable. Worthy of special mention is the head-turning sweet trolley with plenty of choice. There is a large enclosed garden with a children's play area (they are welcome in the dining area at lunchtimes).

THE RED HOUSE

Marsh Benham, nr Newbury.   Tel. (0635) 41637

Location:	Off A4 between Newbury and Hungerford.
Credit cards:	Access, Visa, Amex.
Beers:	Brakspears, Flowers, Marston's Pedigree.
Lagers:	Stella Artois, Heineken.

Examples of bar meals (lunch & evening, 7 days): *homemade pies, ox tongue in madeira sauce, spicy lamb, plaice, vegetable ragout with pasta, sandwiches.*
Examples of restaurant meals (as above): *smoked salmon with scrambled egg, stilton mousse; breast of duck with orange & brandy sauce, escalope of veal, saddle of lamb stuffed with apricots & almonds, fresh halibut, steaks, beef & oyster pie.*

New owners Michael Hoskins and John Goodman have certainly made their mark, an exciting and ever growing menu at reasonable prices attracting an increasing clientele. The attractive 55 seater restaurant is also an excellent venue for wedding receptions and other functions, the more so because of the peaceful rural situation of this 200-years-old thatched freehouse, with a lovely garden bordering a brook. This is ideal walking country, and ramblers often call here for rest and refreshment. Do not be surprised if you see a sky full of colourful balloons, for this is an area also popular with hot air balloonists. Children welcome in garden. Good parking.

THE FIVE BELLS

Wickham, nr Newbury.   Tel. (048 838) 242

Location:	On B4000 Newbury to Lambourn road.
Credit cards:	Access, Visa.
Accommodation:	2 doubles, one twin, one single (all with col. TV).
Beers:	Ushers, Ruddles, Websters. Guinness.
Lagers:	Fosters, Carlsberg.

Examples of meals (bar or restaurant, lunch & evening, 7 days): *avocado prawns, smoked salmon, steaks, fresh local trout, beef Wellington, pigeon pie, excellent cold table, good range of sweets, daily specials. Trad. Sun. lunch.*

Not one to be passed by, this eyecatching and inviting old inn stands on a bend in the road, set in lovely rolling countryside, and is one of the best known in the area. The magnificent thatched roof is matched inside by the low beamed ceiling and log fires, but more important is the convivial atmosphere. This is largely down to Dorrie Channing-Williams, who runs things with friendly efficiency, and with nice little touches like fresh flowers in the washrooms. An excellent reputation for food has been earned with extensive and reasonably priced menus. A function room caters for 40, and the garden has a well equipped children's area (they are also welcome inside). Stay overnight in comfort, and take time to see the picturesque village and Saxon church famed for its 'Elephant' chapel.

THE SWAN

High Street, East Ilsley, nr Newbury.   Tel. (063528) 238
            Location: Off A34, 9 miles north of Newbury. Jnctn 13 of M4.
       Credit cards: Access, Visa.
               Beers: Morlands Bitter & Old Masters. Guinness.
              Lagers: Kaltenberg, Stella Artois.

Examples of bar meals (lunch & evening, 7 days): *steak & kidney pie, steak & onions braised in ale, trout, spare ribs, scampi, wide choice from blackboard.*
Examples of restaurant meals (evenings except Sun. & Mon.): *prawn bisque, 8ozs prime fillet steak, breast of duck, pan fried salmon, sauteed lambs' liver. Good range of sweets. Excellent wine list.*

Nestling in a fold of the Berkshire Downs by the Ridgeway walk, this celebrated 16th century coaching inn is a favoured and easy stopping point on the way to the south coast, and Newbury and Oxford are within easy reach. Recent refurbishment has tastefully blended old and new; the bar is on two levels, on the lower of which is an arched brick fireplace and alcoves. Polished beams, choice carpeting, and elegant tables and chairs combine to most pleasing effect. The medium-sized restaurant is furnished in late Victorian style, full of interesting bric-a-brac. Congenial hosts are Michael and Jenny Connolly, who strive always to ensure good food at fair prices, served with courtesy. They welcome children, and there is a garden and conservatory. Ample parking.

THE RED LION

Downs Road, Compton, nr Newbury.   Tel. (0635) 578370

Location: East of village; follow Streatley signs to Downs Road on left.
Credit cards: Not accepted.
Beers: Morlands Bitter, Old Masters, Mild.
Lagers: Kaltenberg.

Examples of bar meals (every lunch & evening, except Wed. evening): *rump, sirloin & T-bone steaks, lemon sole, chicken Kiev, vegetarian chillis, sandwiches. Traditional Sunday roasts.*

This Downland pub is quite close to the Ridgeway walk, and of course is popular with walkers and locals alike. The comfortable saloon bar is warmed by a log fire, and decorated with racehorse pictures (Compton is a centre for racehorse training). Indoor sports include darts, crib and dominoes, and in summer pig roasts and barbecue events are good outdoor fun in the garden (there are also patios to front and rear). Sunday roasts are particularly popular, but all the food is well-prepared and inexpensive. Robert and Janice Blyth are a friendly couple, who like to exchange banter with their customers. They welcome children and have a play area in the garden. Ample parking.

THE NEW INN

Yattendon Road, Hampstead Norreys, nr Newbury.   Tel. (0635) 201301

Location:	Edge of village.
Credit cards:	Not accepted.
Accommodation:	One single (£18), 2 twins (£28). Caravan Club parking.
Beers:	Morlands.
Lagers:	Kaltenberg, Heineken.

Examples of bar snacks/meals (lunch & evening, 7 days): *homemade steak & kidney pie, chicken & sweetcorn pie, Cottage pie, chilli, farmhouse grill, seafood platter, open sandwiches, ploughman's, salads. Steaks, chicken Kiev, poached salmon, Japanese prawns, crispy vegetables, smoked trout fillets. Specials 3 days per week.*

There used to be an annual badger roast here, many years ago. These days, badger is definitely "off", but the choice is nevertheless very wide, with about 40 items on the bar menu alone. Although there is a separate 'restaurant' menu, including more substantial dishes, there is in fact no dining room as such, all meals being served in either of the two bars. The inn was 'new' 100 years ago when first licensed, but the building itself is over 300 years old, evident from the timber beams and log fires. Aeronautical artefacts acknowledge a following amongst World War II airgunners. In lovely rolling downland, this is horseracing country, with fine walks along the Ridgeway for those who prefer Shanks's pony. Children welcome, and large garden with play area.

THE BEEHIVE

Upper Basildon, nr Pangbourne.   Tel. (0491) 671269

           Location: Opposite village green.
     Credit cards: Access, Visa, Diners.
            Beers: Brakspears, Wadworth, Tetleys, Adnams, Royal Oak.
           Lagers: Stella Artois, Labats, Heineken, Skol, Castlemaine.

Examples of bar meals (lunch & evening, 7 days): *steaks, good range of homemade pies, chicken, scampi, quiche, filled jacket potatoes, ploughman's, salads. Homebaked apple pie, cheesecakes. Traditional 3 course Sunday Lunch £6.95, booking advised.*
Examples of restaurant meals (as above): *smoked salmon, veal cordon bleu, roast loin of lamb, steaks (speciality), lobster 'Beehive', rainbow trout. Treacle & nut pie, double chocolate brandy gateau, 'Beehive' special icecream sundaes.*

High over the Thames Valley in rolling wooded countryside, this handsome freehouse enjoys a loyal local following, so booking is advisable at weekends. One of the favourite attractions is the 'Beehive steak', succulent tender fillet cooked with apple, honey and cider. Michael and Peggy Jones are the force behind this success, based not just on good food, but a pleasant environment in which to savour it. The restaurant is charming, decorated with ornamental plants and tasteful pictures, and the lounge and public bar are also very appealing, having their full complement of panels and beams with brass ornaments, and large fireplace. Children have their own menu, and a play area in the well tended and mature garden. Not an easy one to find, but effort has its rewards.

THE CROWN

Reading Road, Lower Basildon, nr Reading.   Tel. (0491) 671262

Location:	A329, 2 miles from Pangbourne.
Credit cards:	Not accepted.
Beers:	Wadworth 6X, Courage, John Smiths, Maxim Light LA.
Lagers:	Fosters, Kronenbourg.

Examples of bar meals (lunch & evening, 7 days): *steaks (sirloin & fillet), gammon, beef & pepper casserole, chicken cacciatore, scampi, plaice, lasagne, filled jacket potatoes, sandwiches. Children's menu. Trad. Sun. roast. Homemade fruit pie, treacle sponge, spotted dick, apple strudel.*

Situated in the Goring Gap, just five minutes walk from the Thames, The Crown is an ideal spot for rest and recreation before or after visiting beautiful Basildon Park (only 300 yards from here), or Childe Beal Wildlife Park. All the rooms are spacious and very comfortably appointed, with polished tables, period prints or oil paintings and draped curtains and pelmets. One room overlooks the patio and garden, and off the large public bar is a smaller room for non-smokers. Denny and Diane Miller are considerate hosts who like to cater for everyone, and their varied menu proffers anything from a small snack to a full three course meal. They have a family room, but children will prefer the playground in the large mature garden. Parking for 130.

THE FLOWER POT

Ferry Lane, Aston, nr Henley-on-Thames.   Tel. (0491) 574721

Location: Off A423, one mile east of Henley.
Credit cards: Access, Visa.
Accommodation: 2 doubles (one en suite), 2 twins. £38.50/£45 per room.
Beers: Breakspears, Old Ale (winter), Mild (summer). Guinness.
Lagers: Stella Artois, Heineken.

Examples of lunches (7 days): *soup, ratatouille, smoked mackerel, mountain ham, casseroles, ploughman's, sandwiches.*
Examples of evening meals (Tues. - Sat.): *crab stuffed mushrooms, garlic prawns, coq au vin, steaks (plain or au poivre).*

Just 300 yards from Old Father Thames, in a lovely secluded corner of Berkshire, this Victorian pub is a popular watering hole for ramblers and, having its own landing stage, with boating people. Whatever the mode of transport, good food and beer, and a warm welcome from Graham Jones and his staff awaits you. Both bars have been refurbished recently, comfortable but unpretentious. Evening meals are served either in the bars or the dining room. Accommodation is of a high standard, and this is a marvellous spot to stay. Children are welcome (though not in the bars if under 14, by law), and there's a garden to the rear. Ample parking.

THE TWO BREWERS

Wargrave Road, Remenham, nr Henley-on-Thames   Tel. (0491) 574375

Location:	Just past Henley bridge on A321 at fork with A423.
Credit cards:	Not accepted.
Accommodation:	One double en suite (family), 2 twins, one single.
Beers:	Brakspears Bitter, Special, Old Ale. Guinness.
Lagers:	Stella Artois, Heineken.

Examples of bar meals (lunch & evening, 7 days): *moussaka, lasagne, cottage pie, filled jacket potatoes, chicken nuggets with dip, plaice, scampi, toasties, ploughman's, sandwiches.*

The terrace at the front of this 400-years-old inn is only 50 yards from the Thames, so here is an ideal base from which to explore Henley and this stretch of the river. The bedrooms have recently been redecorated and modernised, and prices (for food, also) are very reasonable in what is normally an expensive area. Graham and Deana Godmon are a friendly young couple who will do their best to make your stay a pleasant one. If you are just calling in for a drink and a meal, you will find that there is one central beamed bar, and a number of well furnished separate areas and rooms, including one for families. Ample parking.

THE BULL AT BISHAM

Bisham Village, nr Marlow.   Tel. (0628) 482675

           Location: 600yds from Thames Bridge at Marlow.
      Credit cards: Access, Visa, Diners, Amex.
  Accommodation: 3 doubles in listed cottage.
            Beers: Brakspears, Flowers, Wethereds. Murphys stout.
           Lagers: Stella Artois, Heineken.

Examples of bar meals (lunch & evening, 7 days): *prawn cocktail, smoked salmon, steak & kidney pie, vegetable lasagne, sirloin steak, scampi, filled jacket potatoes, sandwiches, ploughman's.*
Examples of restaurant meals (as above): *sauteed prawns with wild mushrooms, chargrilled fillet steak, chateaubriand, tournedos Rossini, breast of magret duck, poached salmon, Dover sole, chargrilled halibut steak, flambes (house speciality). Sweet trolley & crepes.*

In its 650 years the Bull has been host to many a dignitary, including Elizabeth I, Henry VIII and the Knights Templar. To retain this rich history whilst refurbishing to provide every modern comfort is an aim admirably achieved. The richly upholstered main bar has a seated fireplace alcove and at one end a salad bar servery. A separate cocktail bar with stone brick fireplace leads into the restaurant, where international cuisine of a high order may be enjoyed in luxurious surrounds, with views over the beautiful garden through leaded French windows. A marquee can be attached, and there are newly added conference facilities. The washrooms, incidentally, are palatial! New go-ahead management looks set to enhance an already good reputation and prices are quite reasonable.

THE EAST ARMS HOTEL

Henley Road, Hurley, nr Maidenhead.   Tel. (062 882) 3227
             Location: On A423 Henley to Maidenhead road.
          Credit cards: Access, Visa, Amex.
        Accommodation: 12 bedrooms (7 en suite).
               Beers: Bass Charrington.
               Lagers: Tennents Pilsner & Extra.

Examples of bar meals (all day from 10.30am, 7 days): *pan fried sardines, omelettes, roast pigeon, sirloin steak, duck breast with orange sauce, filled jacket potatoes, salads, pastas, pizzas, chef's blackboard.*
Examples of restaurant meals (lunch Wed. - Fri., evening Tues. - Sat.): *noisettes of lamb, trio of chargrilled fillets (pork, lamb, beef), chateaubriand, steaks, lobster, goujons of lemon sole & seabream. Trad. Sun. lunch.*

One of the most notable small hotels in the Thames Valley, this former coaching inn has been extended and refurbished by owner Nicholas Head with flair and imagination. The new 'Continental' bar and brasserie is fitted out in art deco style, and the charming 'Italian Room' has a fresco of Lake Como. 'Regency' best describes the split level restaurant, beautifully furnished and with French windows leading to vine strewn terrace and attractive garden. Not surprisingly, this is a very popular venue for wedding receptions, and there are also full conference facilities. Dinner dances are held Friday and Saturday evenings, and watch for special events like 60's parties etc (ring for details). Children welcome. Ample parking.

THE WATERMAN'S ARMS

Brocas Street, Eton, Windsor.   Tel. (0753) 861001
Location: Just over Thames bridge at Windsor and turn left.
Credit cards: Not accepted.
Beers: Courage, John Smiths.
Lagers: Kronenbourg, Fosters.

Examples of bar meals (lunch & evening, except Sun. evenings): *lasagne verdi, liver & bacon, beef & potato casserole, vegetable chilli, curry, French vegetable casserole & crusty bread, shepherds pie, scampi, trout, gammon, omelettes, salads, sandwiches. Apple pie, spotted dick, icecream & sorbets.*

A stroll through Royal Windsor and over the pedestrian bridge will bring you to this popular riverside halt, an ideal break before going on to Eton and the famous college. Licensees Jeff and Mary Collibee are an amiable couple but, if asked, will recount chapters in the somewhat lurid history of the pub, starting in 1542, and involving its part in the Great Plague, its days as a workhouse, and recent 'evidence' of ghosts. There's no hint of all this in the very pleasant central bar, with wrought iron work, pictures of rowing scenes, antique furniture and two open fireplaces. There's also a rather nice conservatory and enclosed garden. Well regarded for food and service, and prices very fair. Children welcome. Public car park nearby.

THE DUKE OF EDINBURGH

Woodside Road, Woodside, nr Windsor.　　　　　　　　Tel. (0344) 882736

Location:	Off A332, Ascot to Windsor road.
Credit cards:	Access, Visa.
Beers:	Arkells.
Lagers:	Carling, Carlsberg.

Examples of bar meals (lunch & evening, 7 days): *deep-fried brie, cauliflower cheese & crispy bacon, 8ozs beefburgers, fresh sardines, plaice fillets.*
Examples of restaurant meals (as above): *beef Wellington, lemon sole, poached salmon, monkfish.*

Royal connections go beyond the name; this was once a hunting lodge in Windsor Great Park. The restaurant (children welcome) was the smithy, but now, in the hands of Douglas and Sheila Robinson and son Bruce, it enjoys an enviable reputation for quality food. In both bar and restaurant the speciality is fish, but there are plenty of meat alternatives, and all at very fair prices. The conversion to a pub has been skilfully done; oak timbers, open fire and oil paintings have the right 'olde worlde' feel, and there are several nicely furnished alcoves. Ideally situated for a visit before or after a view of the horseracing and funny hats at Ascot. Ample parking.

THE UNION INN

17 Crimp Hill, Old Windsor.   Tel. (0753) 861955

Location: From jnctn 13 of M25 follow A30 signs to 'Victoria' roundbt, then A308 twrds Windsor. Turn off at St Leonards Road - ¹/₂ m to Crimp Hill.
Credit cards: Access, Visa, Amex.
Accommodation: 8 doubles, 4 singles, all en suite.
Beers: Theakstons, Flowers Original, Courage Best, John Smiths.
Lagers: Red Stripe, Stella Artois, Heineken, Hofmeister, Fosters, Miller Lite.

Examples of bar meals (lunch & evenings, Mon. - Sat.) *coq au vin, ribsteak, filled jacket potatoes, chilli, many daily blackboard specials.*
Examples of restaurant meals (lunchtime except Sat., evenings except Sun.): *Scotch rump steak garni, fillet of veal, grilled salmon, fillets of sole mornay, roast pheasant, roast rack of lamb, vegetarian dishes, tempting sweet trolley. Trad. Sun. lunch.*

This is one of the most popular inns in the area, the reward for the transformation effected by Fred and Sheila Ward when they took over in '85. Accommodation, cooking, beers and atmosphere are all first rate. The attractive beamed restaurant seats 50 and offers an extensive a la carte or table d'hote, while in the L-shaped bar good value meals and snacks are served, to be enjoyed perhaps around the large log fireplace. Relax with a pint on the luxurious Chesterfield, or catch some sun on the delightful south terrace, then explore nearby historic Runnymede or Windsor. Children welcome. Good parking.

THE BARLEY MOW

Cox Green Lane, Cox Green, Maidenhead.   Tel. (0628) 29986

Location:	Off M4 via A423(M), follow Cox Green signs.
Credit cards:	Not accepted.
Beers:	Ruddles, Websters, Trumans.
Lagers:	Budweiser, Carlsberg, Fosters, Holsten.

Examples of bar meals (lunch Mon. - Sat., evening Mon. - Fri.): *special kebabs, garlic mushrooms, scampi, Mexican burger, ploughman's, filled jacket potatoes. Chocolate fudge cake.*

Although the old farming village of Cox Green has been swallowed by the expansion of Maidenhead, The Barley Mow has withstood the rapid changes around it and retains much of its rustic character. From the one long bar Val, Andrew and Helena Trusler take pride in serving excellent ales and substantial helpings of homemade food - witness the diplomas displayed for Best Cellar award, Excellence of Food, and even Best Floral Display. In addition to regular 60's discos and occasional live entertainment, there are the usual pub games, and the darts team is entered in the national championship. For a very lively and friendly pub in the Maidenhead area, with good value food, look no further. Children welcome. Small garden. Ample parking.

THE JOLLY GARDENER

Moneyrow Green, Holyport, nr Maidenhead.   Tel. (0628) 22933
        Location: On B3204 Windsor-Twyford road, 5 miles west of Windsor.
    Credit cards: Access, Visa, Amex.
            Beers: Theakstons, Youngers, Tartan Special.
          Lagers: Becks, McEwans.

Examples from lunchtime menu (7 days): *homemade smoked mackerel pate, chicken Portuguese, homecooked ham, homemade chicken ham & mushroom pie, spicy chilli pie, macaroni cheese, breaded haddock, ploughman's, sandwiches, salads. Sherry trifle, apricot crumble, hot chocolate fudge cake, passion cake, Mississippi mud pie. Trad. Sun. roast.*
Examples from evening menu (7 days): *Many dishes as above, steaks, honey roast duck, lamb chops, grilled trout and almonds, chicken Kiev.*

In a pleasant rural location only a few miles from Windsor, the pub has recently undergone extensive refurbishment. The results are most pleasing, a nice blend of the old and the new. There is one long bar, plenty of space, but with alcoves for intimacy. The brick pillars and walls are adorned with tasteful pictures, and the whole is light and airy. Landlord Chris Leaver has been in catering 14 years, including service on the QE 2, and with wife Jill has worked a remarkable transformation here. Their growing clientele will vouch for the friendly atmosphere and the good value of the varied menu. Children are welcome in the well tended garden, or inside eating with parents. Ample parking.

THE BELL

The Street, Waltham St Lawrence, nr Reading. Tel. (0734) 341788
           Location: Village centre, opp. church.
   Credit cards: Access, Visa.
           Beers: Brakspears, Wadworth, Adnams, Marston's Pedigree.
          Lagers: Stella Artois, Castlemaine XXXX, Lowenbrau.

Examples of bar meals (lunchtimes Mon. - Sat.): *various homemade pies (including steak & kidney, beef & venison, chicken & mushroom, chicken ham & leek), scampi, special 'Bell' pizzas.*
Examples of dining room meals (evenings Tues. - Sat.): *roast rack of lamb, chicken en croute, chicken fillet with pate in bacon and cooked in puff pastry, gammon steak, pies as lunchtime.*

Here is one of Berkshire's most renowned pubs, in the heart of an old village mentioned in the Domesday Book. Its 14th century timbers are surprisingly well preserved, and combine felicitously with the panelled walls hung with historic prints, open log fires and antique longcase clock. The dining room could be described as Edwardian in style, but whether eating here or in either bar one can rely on quality food and well kept ales, earning a recommendation from Egon Ronay. Genial hosts Spencer and Helen Myers particularly welcome visitors, and permit children in the garden. Parking to front and rear.

THE PLOUGH & HARROW

Newell Green, Warfield, nr Bracknell.   Tel. (0344) 42102

Location:	Jnctn A3095 and A3034, one mile north of Bracknell.
Credit cards:	Not accepted.
Beers:	Morlands Bitter, Old Masters, Revival. Guinness.
Lagers:	Kaltenberg, Stella Artois.

Examples of bar meals (all day from 9am, 7 days): *full English or continental breakfast, lasagne, chillies, curries (very hot! Ice water provided), omelettes, cider-baked gammon, homemade pies, liver & bacon with herby dumplings. Traditional Sunday lunch.*

First impressions are favourable; pleasant rural surrounds and with hanging baskets and a rock garden, and inside lives up to expectations. The 18th century pub is not lacking in character, and has a spacious, comfortable lounge with many interesting pictures and abundant brass ornaments. Open fires warm both this and the public bar, where locals gather to play crib and dominoes, and chat with landlady Maggie Cocks. Often described as 'vivacious' and 'ebullient', she is clearly warmly regarded, and with the staff works hard to provide good value and quality, with an emphasis on old English dishes. Very few pubs provide meals all day, and this must be a boon to locals and office workers. Children welcome if eating with parents. Garden. Ample parking.

THE CASTLE INN

Church Hill, Hurst, nr Reading.   Tel. (0734) 340034

Location:	Village centre, opp. church.
Credit cards:	Not accepted.
Beers:	Courage, Directors, John Smiths. Plus Guinness, dry cider.
Lagers:	Fosters, Hofmeister, Kronenbourg, Carlton LA.

Examples of bar meals (lunch & evening, 7 days): *steak & kidney pie, boiled beef with carrots & dumplings, scampi, various casseroles, roasts. Variety of homemade puddings.*

The village has a chequered history going back to Norman and even Saxon times. In the centre stands the Castle, said to be 700 years old, but certainly at least 500. On its south side is to be found the bowling green, founded by Charles 1 in 1628, and played on by his son and Nell Gwynne. For further details, consult landlady Norma Hose, who obviously loves the place and will discourse at length on the subject. She observes the unimpeachable tradition of serving good ale and wholesome English fare. Swords and hunting horns adorn the beams in the lounge bar, warmed by a log fire. One concession to modernity is the pool table in the public bar. Outside there are hanging baskets with a patio garden overlooking the bowling green, and watching a game whilst quaffing ale on a balmy summer evening is a blissful experience. Children's room. Good parking.

THE TWO POPLARS

118 Finchampstead Road, Wokingham.   Tel. (0734) 780590
            Location: A321, one mile south of Wokingham centre.
        Credit cards: Access, Visa, Amex.
              Beers: Morlands.
              Lagers: Kaltenberg, Stella Artois, Dansk LA.

Examples of bar meals (lunchtime every day, evenings except Sunday): *prawn cocktail, smoked pepper mackerel, calamari rings, lasagne, homemade steak & kidney pie, chicken curry, chilli, scampi, various salads and daily specials. Good choice of sweets.*

This easily accessible and spacious pub has two large bars with dining area, all carpeted and with well upholstered, comfortable furniture. Connected by an arch, both bars are timber beamed and panelled. Alternatively, there is the newly constructed conservatory, light and airy. Hosts Paul and Ann Garland are a very friendly and cheerful pair, whose pleasure is to serve well-prepared food at reasonable prices. They also stock the full range of Morlands beers, including 'Old Masters' (the local favourite), and a good selection of wines. Children are most welcome in the family room, or better still can vent their energies on the garden amusements. Large car park.

THE WARREN INN

Forest Road, Wokingham.   Tel. (0344) 483773

      Location: On B3034 one mile north of Wokingham.
Credit cards: Access, Visa, Diners.
        Beers: Bass, Charrington IPA, Wadworth 6X.
       Lagers: Carling, Tennents Pilsner and Extra.

Examples of bar meals (lunch & evening, 7 days): *shepherds pie, sirloin steak, scampi, pork chop, roast topside, salads, sandwiches, ploughman's.*
Examples of restaurant meals (evenings Wed. - Sat.): *garlic mushrooms, avocado with smoked salmon mousse, mussels in white wine & garlic; chicken breast stuffed with garlic butter, baked trout filled with prawns & mushrooms, cold seafood platter, fillet steak, rack of lamb, fresh salmon cutlet poached in wine & herbs.*

Charrington's 'Pub of the Year', The Warren Inn has achieved such an accolade by the quality of bar food and ales, as well as hospitality and general levels of comfort. Colin and Marion Larter have obviously been successful with their formula of basing menus on English homecooking, using fresh meat, fish and vegetables. The 40 seater 'stable' restaurant, replete with oak beams and pillars, is a most attractive setting in which to enjoy the generous helpings. The split level lounge bar is also rather agreeable, with panelled walls, oak beams and pillars and brick fireplace. Children have an area set aside, and a well equipped play area in the large shaded garden. The inn has graced this pleasant part of the county since the reign of George III.

THE TROUT INN

St Johns Bridge, Lechlade-on-Thames.   Tel. (0367) 52313
      Location: 1 mile east of Lechdale, on A417
  Credit cards: Access, Visa.
       Beers: Courage Best, Directors, John Smith.
      Lagers: Carlton, Fosters, Kronenberg.

Examples of bar meals (lunch & evening, 7 days): *garlic courgettes, chicken nuggets with curry dip, tagliatelli in herbed white sauce; homemade pies, chilli, curry, rump steak, seafood crumble, seafood pancakes, fresh local trout, vegetarian meals, children's menu.* Examples from restaurant (Wed. - Sat.): *smoked prawns in lime & tarragon dip, trout with Grand Marnier brandy & almond sauce, chicken & mushroom pie, beef Wellington, chargrilled steaks, cashew nut roast with tomato sauce.*

Built around 1220 (one of the oldest in the county) as an almshouse, on the banks of the river Thames and renamed The Trout Inn in 1704. The pub still holds the Royal Charter ancient fishery rights and controls two miles of trout and coarse fishing waters. Wooden tables and settles, fishing prints, old photographs and stuffed pike and trout on the walls complement this lovely old inn perfectly. Bob and Penny Warren serve an excellent range of food and wine, with fresh trout, needless to say, a regular. A marquee is available for weddings and other functions, with full catering including vegetarian menu. Live jazz every Tuesday evening from 8-11. Children welcome, and have their own separate menu. Large gardens and ample parking.

THE BULL HOTEL

The Market Place, Fairford.   Tel. (0285) 712535/712217

Location: Town centre, just off A417.
Credit cards: Access, Visa, Diners, Amex.
Accommodation: 14 doubles, 5 twins, 2 singles.
Beers: Arkells, 2 B's, 3 B's. Guinness.
Lagers: Stella Artois, Carling.

Examples of bar meals (lunch & evening, 7 days): *smoked prawns with avocado dip, terrine of salmon & asparagus salad; stir fried fillet of gingered beef, lamb kebabs with spicy sauce & rice, homemade pie, deep fried plaice, fresh tortelloni filled with ricotta cheese in cream sauce.*
Examples of restaurant meals (as above): *roast quail filled with smoked salmon mousse on raspberry coulis, filo pastry parcels of scallops & wild mushrooms in cream sauce; breast of chicken filled with mango & sauteed in coconut, medallion of halibut in duo of pepper sauces, homemade nut roast.*

Along one side of the famous market square you will find this marvellous example of a Cotswold town hotel. Much of the building dates from the 15th century, when it was a monk's chanting house. The first record of its use as a hotel was in 1745, and now, as then, its position commends itself to business people, and The Bull Room comes well equipped to deal with conferences, weddings etc. The private visitor is also well cosseted in warm, relaxing surrounds, with a wide choice of homecooked food, from fresh local produce, both in bar and restaurant. Stay in a comfortable bedroom (perhaps with 4-poster or sunken bath), then try trout fishing on 1 1/2 miles on the Coln.

THE VILLAGE PUB

Barnsley, nr. Cirencester.   Tel. (028 574) 421
           Location: Village centre, A433 Cirencester - Burford.
       Credit cards: Access, Visa.
     Accommodation: 4 dbls, 2 twins (4 en suite). £25 single, £38 dbl.
              Beers: Wadworth 6X, Flowers IPA, Whitbread Best.
             Lagers: Stella Artois, Castlemaine, Heineken.

Examples of bar meals (available lunch & evening 7 days): *Scotch smoked salmon, steak & kidney pie, original Gloucester sausages, breadcrumbed plaice, chilli, sandwiches, salads, ploughman's.*
Examples of restaurant meals (as above): *homemade game pate, beef in Elderberry wine, bream in crab sauce, Covent Garden pie (mixed vegetables in wholemeal crust), steaks, local Bibury trout. Raspberry syllabub, treacle tart & custard.*

Lovely surrounds, excellent food and drink, very comfortable accommodation, and a good dose of tradition make for a very satisfying visit. Blending in unobtrusively with the very pretty cottages either side of the road, the pub is attractively furnished, with sporting prints and old farm implements decorating the walls. Three log fires will thaw you in winter, aided by Merrydown wine (like sparkling peach, elderberry or damson) for which it is well known. In summer, relax in the sheltered courtyard, and decide what to eat from the outside servery, to be washed down, perhaps, with some potent Cotswold cider. The food in both bar and restaurant is always imaginative and reasonably priced. Vegetarians catered for, and check the blackboard for daily specials. Children welcome. Large car park. Combine with a visit to nearby Barnsley House and beautiful gardens.

THE GREYHOUND INN

Ashton Road, Siddington, Cirencester.   Tel: (0285) 653573.
- Location: Off A419, one mile from Cirencester.
- Credit cards: Not accepted.
- Beers: Wadworth IPA, Wadworth 6X, Tanglefoot.
- Lagers: Heineken, Stella Artois.

Examples of bar meals (available lunchtime and evening, 7 days): *fresh mushrooms in garlic butter,smoked salmon, pint or half pint of prawns; full range of steaks and homemade dishes, including steak & kidney pudding, chicken curry, vegetable gratin; jam roly-poly & custard.*

A genuine Cotswold stone pub managed by Robert and Elaine Flaxman, a friendly Yorkshire couple. The large lounge and public bar, with brick floors, open log fires, oak beams and walls decorated with old farming implements provide a welcoming and cosy environment. This popular pub is also a big hit with local business people, who no doubt enjoy the opportunity to eat out in the garden during the summer. The menu is very extensive; a wealth of salads, 6 choices of omelettes and 9 different fillings for jacket potatoes in addition to the hot dishes. Blackboard specials are changed daily. Children welcome in the garden, in the summer. Large car park. Darts and skittles in public bar.

THE RAGGED COT INN

Hyde, Chalford, nr Stroud.   Tel. (0453) 884643

Location:	off A 419 nr Aston Down airfield.
Credit cards:	Access, Visa, Amex.
Accommodation:	8 twins, 2 doubles, all en suite. From £39 single, £49 dbl. Weekend breaks from £22 pp per night.
Beers:	Boddingtons, Pedigree, Old Spot, Theakstons, Youngers.
Lagers:	Becks, Harp, McEwans.

Examples of bar meals (available 12 - 2pm, 7 - 9:30pm (9pm Sundays): *cauliflower cheese with crusty roll, steak & kidney pie, lasagne, tipsy beef in red wine & brandy sauce, sandwiches, salads.*
Examples of restaurant meals (available as above): *sherried mushrooms, creamed kidneys in port, Caribbean prawn salad, chicken stuffed with pate, loin of pork with apricot & orange, whole lemon sole, steaks, 3 vegetarian choices. Chocoloate roulade, orange & kiwi gateau, Brazilian cheesecake.*

One of the first landlords of this 17th century stone inn is said to have fatally pushed his wife and child off the stairs, en route to his second job as highwayman. Their ghosts rose up even as he was arrested (to his alarm and the constables'). Hosts since 1986, Mike and Margaret Case are rather friendlier than their distant predecessor, though Mike does have experience of spirits - he was in the trade for 20 years. With outstanding food and personal attention they have established an excellent reputation, and the dining room extension was much needed. Don't even try to resist the irresistible sweets! Beautiful garden, and new superior bedrooms - superb for weekend break.

THE AMBERLEY INN

Amberley, nr Stroud.   Tel. (045 387) 2565/2777

Location:	1/2 mile off A46 on Minchinhampton Common.
Credit cards:	Mastercard, Visa, Amex.
Accommodation:	14 rooms, all en suite and with full facilities. Some with fine views over Woodchester valley.
Beers:	Wadworth, Hook Norton, Butcombe.
Lagers:	Stella Artois, Carlsberg.

Examples of bar snacks (lunch & evening, 7 days): *scampi, pizzas, ploughman's, salads, sandwiches, omelettes.*
Examples of restaurant meals (as above): *button mushrooms filled with pate, North sea prawns; poached Severn salmon, escalope of veal in mushroom & sherry sauce, tournedos Rossini, sliced breast of duckling in peppercorn & brandy sauce.*

For those touring, or seeking outdoor activities, The Amberley Inn cannot be faulted. Slimbridge Wildfowl trust is nearby, as is the Roman Villa at Yanworth, Sudeley Castle, and Cheltenham and Gloucester. It's great walking country, but there are also two golf courses, horse riding, and the inn has its own squash and tennis courts, free to residents by advance booking. One of the Best Western independent consortium, it was among the first to receive a British Tourist Authority country hotel commendation. Facilities for small business or private functions are excellent, but this lovely old inn lends itself to relaxation - in the well tended gardens, perhaps. Visit also the sister Hare & Hounds Hotel at Westonbirt.

THE ROSE & CROWN INN

Nympsfield, Stonehouse.   Tel. (0453) 860240

Location:	Village centre.
Credit cards:	Access, Visa.
Accommodation:	Three family rooms, one double room.
Beers:	Uley, Marstons, Wadworth, Whitbread.
Lagers:	Becks, Carlsberg, Heineken.

Examples of bar meals (lunch & evening, 7 days): *triple decker sandwich with choice of fillings, filled jacket potatoes, ploughman's, 'farmer's boy feast', chargrilled chicken, steak & kidney pie, Welsh faggots, rainbow trout, scampi, beef goulash, beef & ale stew, curries, nut fettucini, steaks.*

Once there were five inns in this quiet Cotswolds village; there remains just this one. However, quality is surely more important than quantity and this 300 year old coaching inn is certainly not short of that. The food is wholesome and combines traditional English with nice 'n' spicy dishes from other parts, served with rice and vegetables or a hunk of fresh bread and butter. Wash it down with a jug of well kept 'Old Spot' local ale from Uley brewery in neighbouring village, which won the Camra award last year, and have a look at the old photos of past village life which decorate the walls. The smaller of the two bars is available for private parties (16 seated, 25 buffet), and look out for the annual floral display for which the inn is famous. A true, friendly village local, with that personal touch from Bob and Linda Woodman. Children welcome.

THE PICKWICK INN

Lower Wick, nr Dursley.   Tel. (0453) 810259
>   Location: 1 ¹/₂ miles off A38 (opp. side to Berkeley turn-off).
>   Credit cards: Not accepted.
>   Beers: Theakstons, Bass, Butcombe.
>   Lagers: Carlsberg, Fosters.

Examples of bar meals (lunch & evening, 7 days): *mushrooms in garlic sauce, steak, lasagne, curry, pork chop in brandy & peppercorn sauce, steak & kidney pie, poached mussels in cream & garlic sauce, pan fried langoustines with garlic bread, homemade pepperoni pizza with salad, leek & potato bake. Fruit crumble, raspberry pavlova, creme brulee.*
Sundays: *roasts, fresh Severn salmon, saute of lamb with coriander. Pineapple & peach shortbread with cream. Some dishes as above.*

Tremendous value and outstanding home cooking have made this one of the best known and admired pubs in the area. The highly original menus are chalked on a blackboard and revised regularly (note there is a separate Sunday menu). There's a friendly, well used feel to the place, too, with its original timbers and brickwork (dating from 1763), and an open wood fire. Both the bars are spacious and appealing, having wooden tables, chairs and benches, and one with a snug. Colin and Jane Pickford are friendly hosts, always to hand, and they welcome children. They have a large, safe garden, and plenty of parking space.

THE NEW INN

Waterley Bottom, North Nibley, Dursley.   Tel: (0453) 543659
- **Location:** Off A4153, south of Dursley.
- **Credit cards:** Not accepted.
- **Accommodation:** 1 twin, 1 double room with T.V. & tea making facilities. (Rooms recently refurbished).
- **Beers:** Cotleigh W.B., Cotleigh Tawny, Greene King Abbot, Smiles Best, Smiles Exhibition, Theakstons Old Peculier.
- **Lagers:** Lowenbrau, Castlemaine.

Examples from bar menus (lunch and evening, available 7 days a week): *Smoked trout homemade pate, toasted sandwiches, ploughman's, chilli con carne & hot cottage loaf, steak with onions, quiche and salad.*

A most personal welcome, cheerfully given by Ruby Sainty, inspires the amiable atmosphere at this peaceful country pub. Set in a valley, the views of the surrounding hillside and rambling woods are superb. Picture windows look out from the warmly furnished lounge onto an immaculately kept garden, nestling below the hillside slopes. The considerable range of real ales and ciders is one of the best in the area, and the quality of draught Guinness is espicially noted. Antique hand pump beer engines form part of an interesting collection of "breweriana". The public bar has an interesting selection of games such as dominoes, shove halfpenny and quizzes. The food is exceptionally good value and is homemade on the premises. Bed and breakfast is also good value.

HUNTERS HALL INN

Kingscote, nr Tetbury.   Tel. (0453) 860393 Fax (0453) 860707
Location: On A4135 Dursley/Tetbury road.
Credit cards: Access, Visa, Diners, Amex.
Accommodation: 12 twins/doubles, all en suite & with full facilities. 2
fitted for disabled. From £44 single, £54 double. 2 day
breaks £49 pp or £79 incl. a la carte dinner.
Beers: Bass, Hook Norton, Smiles, Uley Old Spot.
Lagers: Carling, Tennants.

Examples of blackboard bar meals (lunch & evening, 7 days): *homemade soup, h/m steak & kidney pie with cheese & garlic potatoes, chicken & mushroom pancake, lamb curry, full cold table. H/m choc. mousse, treacle tart.*
Examples of restaurant meals (as above): *seafood selection, chicken Alabama; steaks, fillet of lamb in mint & cream sauce, medallions of venison in black cherry sauce, vegetarian dish, fresh fish of the day.*

This beautiful creeper-clad Tudor building has long been a superior, elegant establishment, rated highly for food and atmosphere in most major guides, but now also offers first class accommodation in a conversion from the old stable block and blacksmith's shop. Ideally situated for business people and tourists alike, the M4 and M5 are only 15 mins away, and Slimbridge Wildfowl Trust, Westonbirt Arboretum, Berkeley Castle, Badminton House and the glories of The Cotswolds are all close by, as well as every outdoor activity. A function room can accommodate up to 50, for conferences etc, and for the family there's a large garden with play area and barbecues in summer. Proprietor David Barnett-Roberts supervises with a personal touch.

THE KING'S HEAD

Lynch Road, France Lynch, Chalford, nr Stroud.　　　　　Tel. (0453) 882225

Location:	Off A419 via Bisley, right at hilltop.
Credit cards:	Access, Visa, Mastercard, Eurocard.
Beers:	Theakstons, Tetleys, Archers, Courage Best & Directors.
Lagers:	Kronenbourg 1664, Fosters, Carlsberg.

Examples of bar meals (12 to 2pm Mon. - Sat. 7 to 9:30pm Tues. - Sat.): *deep fried king prawns & squid with selection of dips, stilton & bacon pancakes, tuna & pasta bake with garlic bread, grilled trout. Homemade crunchie icecream, homemade cherry & brandy pie.*
Examples from grillstone menu (as above): *sirloin steak, salmon steak with satay sauce, mixed grill, tenderloin of pork (with bacon, pineapple & bananas).*

Grillstones are an exciting new eating experience, yet derive from the oldest form of cooking. Brought to your table, they release heat for up to 40 mins, so you can enjoy a leisurely and delicious freshly prepared meal to suit yourself. A barbecue will be another new attraction this summer, in a special area in the pleasant garden. Andrew Farrall is the man behind these innovations - he runs this hospitable rural pub with his parents, and is always flexible where special requests are concerned. Originally two cottages, it's on a lovely spot, with fine views over the Golden Valley. Understandably, it is very popular, but overspill can be accommodated in a second bar, once the loft, which can also serve as a private function room. Children welcome (play area in garden). Darts and pool.

THE BUTCHERS ARMS

Oakridge Lynch, nr Stroud.   Tel. (028 576) 371

Location:	Village centre. Off A419, turn right just before Bisley.
Credit cards:	Access, Visa.
Beers:	Butcombe, Burton, Ruddles, Tetley, Archers Best.
Lagers:	Lowenbrau, Skol.

Examples from menus (available every lunchtime in bar, and in Stable Room Wed. - Sat. evenings): *homemade cottage pie, cauliflower cheese, stout beef pie (prime beef with Guinness & kidneys), Gloucestershire sausages, jacket potatoes with cheese topping, ploughman's, daily specials. Trad. Sun. lunch.*

Nestling in a picturesque hillside Cotswolds village, this cosy 18th century stone pub takes its name from the butchers shop it once was. The central bar serves both the charming lounge, with crackling fire and timber beams (just enough headroom!), and the newly converted 'Stable Room', where evening meals are served. The cooking is recognised for value and quality, the ales no less so, but equally important is the friendly atmosphere, fostered by partners Peter and Brian Coupe. They set tables in the sizeable garden in summer, but darts or the skittle alley may divert you indoors. A little tricky to find, but definitely worth the effort. Large car park.

THE ROYAL OAK

St Mary's Street, Painswick.   Tel: (0452) 813129

Location: Village centre
Credit cards: Not accepted.
Beers: Flowers original, Whitbread.
Lagers: Stella Artois, Heineken.

Examples from daily menus (available lunch & evening every day except Sunday): *fresh fish dishes every Thursday. Chilli con carne and garlic bread, cold fresh salmon and salad, cauliflower cheese with grilled bacon and jacket potato, home made lasagne, chicken Kiev, excellent range of sandwiches, home made soup and ploughmans.*

The Royal Oak, located in the heart of the glorious village of Painswick, is an ideal place for a break when walking in the Cotswolds. Painswick is famous for it's churchyard with ninety nine Yew trees, and this charming old pub blends agreeably with the natural English beauty of the village. During the summer one can enjoy a sheltered courtyard. Designed to catch the sun, it is filled with colourful plants, pots of geranium and climbing wisteria. In the winter an open fire blazes in the massive chimney, which divides the lounge in two, and there is a second bar leading off from the lounge, reached by a richly panelled oak door. The Morris family has a well earned reputation for serving very good quality, freshly prepared food with a wide and varied selection always on offer.

THE WOODMAN - PHILEAS FOGG'S BISTRO

Parkend, Lydney.
Tel. (0594) 563273

Location:	Village centre.
Credit cards:	Access, Visa.
Accommodation:	2 doubles, 2 singles.
Beers:	Marstons, Flowers.
Lagers:	Stella Artois, Heineken. Plus Bulmers trad. cider.

Examples of bar meals (available 12 - 2pm, 6:15 - 10pm in summer, from 7:15 in winter): *homemade soups, local rainbow trout, lasagne, steak & kidney pie, monkfish pie, steaks, chicken curry, vegetarian dishes.*

Examples of bistro meals - German, but nationality changes bi-monthly (available as above): *poached fish fillet in dill sauce, pork chop with knackwurst sausage & potatoes hot pot style, grilled rump steak with spicy sour cream sauce, German sausages in mixed onion salad, pheasant in brandy sauce, vegetable medley, pan fried veal escalope in breadcrumbs.*

The inn passed into the hands of Keith and Pat over two years ago - a nice, traditional pub, but something different and special was their aim. The fruit of their head scratching was the bistro, with a national theme changing every two months. International cuisine was meticulously researched, embassies were approached. The food has to be fresh, nothing frozen, except perhaps Italian icecream, and only high quality ingredients used. Even the decor and music were combined to suit. The same standards apply to the 'Woodman Fayre', selected from the blackboard in the main bar. Now, with the introduction of midweek breaks, guests can sample their way through the menu!

THE RED LION

Arlingham, nr Gloucester.   Tel. (0452) 740269
        Location: Village centre, off A38.
    Credit cards: Not accepted.
            Beers: Smiles, Tetley, Bass, Theakstons, plus guest.
           Lagers: Harlech, Fosters, Kronenbourg.

Examples of bar meals (lunch & evening, 7 days): *ploughman's, baps with various fillings, faggots with mushy peas, garlic bread with toasted cheese, Arlingham chicken (not Sun. lunch), scampi, spinach & mushroom lasagne, mushroom & nut fettucini, various pies. Treacle sponge with custard, apricot crumble flan with cream.*

This is one for real ale buffs. The Packman family is justly proud of the choice and quality of the beers, but also earns praise for the bar meals, no-nonsense and very tasty. An area has been set aside to enjoy them in the recently refurbished main bar, and without electronic conversation-killers to spoil it. Traditional entertainments in the public bar include darts and shove ha'penny, and with its own bar is one of the best skittle alleys in the county – be good or be beaten! In summary, an unpretentious, friendly local, 17th century and in a very pretty village which is a little off the beaten track, but well worth seeking out. Car parking to rear.

THE COLESBOURNE INN

Colesbourne, nr Cheltenham.　　　　　Tel. (024 287) 376/396　Fax　(024 287) 397

Location:	On A435 between Cheltenham & Cirencester.
Credit cards:	Access, Visa, Diners, Amex.
Accommodation:	8 doubles (£44 per night incl.), 2 singles (£25), all en suite. Getaway breaks £75pp (2 nights), £110 (3 nights), £135 (4 nights), includes 3 course a la carte dinner & wine.
Beers:	Wadworth Old Timer, 6X, IPA, North Gate.
Lagers:	Stella Artois, Heineken.

Examples from menu (lunch & evening, 7 days): *local smoked salmon, homemade Colesbourne pate, homemade steak Guinness & mushroom pie, supreme of chicken with paw-paws on light curry sauce, platter of mixed seafood with a cream dill & lovage sauce, prime steaks, vegetarian pancakes, salads, jacket potatoes, daily specials. Homemade sweets.*

This is one of those excellent country inns that make The Cotswolds such a pleasure to explore. It is an area steeped in history - the Emperor Gratian was once lord of the manor here. The inn itself is 'only' about 200 years old, and the stable block has been converted to very comfortable bedrooms, rating four crowns from the Tourist Board. Eric and Mary Bird and staff offer a genuine, friendly welcome to allcomers. The food, mostly local produce, is of the first order, and may be enjoyed informally by the fire in the atmospheric bar, or in the recently extended 'Brambles' restaurant with patio, overlooking lovely countryside. AA specially selected, rated by Egon Ronay and most other guides. Children welcome.

THE FOX & HOUNDS INN & RESTAURANT

Bredon, Tewkesbury.   Tel. (0684) 72377/72471
      Location: Village centre.
  Credit cards: Access, Visa, Cardnet.
        Beers: Flowers, Marstons.
        Lagers: Stella Artois, Heineken.

Examples of bar meals (lunch & evenings, except Sunday evening): *various ploughman's, salads. Assorted cold meats & platters. Individual homecooked dishes: smoked haddock & mushroom mornay, steak & kidney pie, braised BBQ pork ribs, pot of savoury mushrooms, liver & onions, baked leeks & ham with cheese sauce.*
Extensive a la carte (available as above): *asparagus pancake with cheese sauce, crispy fried soft roes, garlic mushrooms; chicken breast filled with pineapple & stilton, steaks with various sauces, pheasant casserole, fresh fish, plus daily blackboard specials & puddings. All is fresh (vegetables from Vale of Evesham) and cooked to order.*

In a picturebook village, this timbered and thatched inn provides a comfortable respite for holidaymakers, whether straight from the waterborne delights of the adjacent river Avon, or from hill walking or pony trekking around lovely Bredon Hill. Yet it is just 10 minutes from the motorway, and is also popular with business people. Landlord Michael Hardwick, whose family has run the business for over 40 years, has concentrated over the last two decades on successfully establishing a reputation for quality food. The separate and luxurious restaurant is candlelit and enticing for a leisurely 'diner a deux', while in the lounge there's truly a cornucopia of freshly prepared bar meals and snacks from the buffet and kitchen for those in a hurry. Pub games in the main bar. Children and small animals catered for in garden (with picnic tables and barbecue). Ample parking.

THE FARMERS ARMS

Apperley, nr Tewkesbury.   Tel. (045 278) 307
      Location: On B4213 off A38.
  Credit cards: Not accepted.
        Beers: Hook Norton, Wadworth, Flowers, Bass.
      Lagers: Stella Artois, Heineken.

Examples of bar meals (12 - 2:30pm, 6 - 10:30pm, 7 days): *homemade beef & ale pie, lasagne, lamb in orange & ginger sauce, Somerset pork, beef in red wine, ploughman's. Homemade apple pie, bread & butter pudding.*
Examples of restaurant meals (available as above): *seafood cocktail, gravlaks, chicken satay, Farmers special mixed grill, steaks, whole grilled lemon sole, daily specials, vegetarian by request. Death by chocolate, grasshopper pie.*

A friendly inn, not spoiled by tweeness, quietly situated yet convenient for Tewkesbury. Geoff and Carole run this Cotswold gem with the family in mind. They serve good portions of fresh food - nothing frozen, nothing fried, and nothing left! (the famous mixed grill presents a particular challenge, though). Daily attractions are announced on a blackboard over the log fire. An extension to the dining area is to be added shortly to accommodate increasing numbers. Offspring may frolic in the secure beer garden and play area, leaving inconsolable parents in peace! Ample parking.

THE MOUNT INN

Stanton, nr Broadway.
Tel. (038 673) 316

      Location: B4632, through village to hill top.
Credit cards: Not accepted.
        Beers: Donningtons. Plus scrumpy cider.
      Lagers: Carlsberg pilsner & export.

Examples of bar meals (12 - 2pm, 7 days. 7 - 9pm, except Suns): *cow pie, steak & kidney pie, chicken & sweetcorn, cauliflower cheese & potato bake, ratatouille lasagne, ploughman's, toasties. Figgy pudding & brandy sauce, blackberry & apple pie. Blackboard specials.*

As the name suggests. the inn stands on a hill affording a stunning panorama of the exquisite Cotswold villages, and beyond to the Malverns. The view is best from the terrace, but the large extension has cinemascope windows. The original building is circa 1640, with black sturdy beams, oak wall seats, and footworn flagstones that tell their own story. Should the view pall, darts, dominoes, shove ha'penny or cribbage will entertain, or try your hand on one of the boules courts. Food is always fresh, never fried, and good value. Colin Johns' inn is featured in well known guides, and he welcomes children. Ample parking.

THE HORSE & GROOM

Upper Oddington, Moreton-in-Marsh   Tel. (0451) 30584

Location:	Village centre.
Credit cards:	Access, Visa.
Accommodation:	4 doubles, 2 twins, 1 family. From £19.50 pp.
Beers:	Hook Norton, Wadworth 6X, John Smiths, Worthington Best.
Lagers:	Stella Artois, Castlemaine XXXX.

Examples of bar meals (12 – 2pm, 6.30 – 9.30pm, 7 days): *delicious filled sandwiches (lunch only), daily blackboard specials eg plaice stuffed with prawns, tagliatelle Bolognese with garlic bread, lamb & cherry casserole, broccoli & cheese mornay with salad.*
Examples of restaurant meals (7 – 9pm, 7 days): *deep fried brie parcels, Fox's choice (half roast duck in apricot & brandy sauce), Oddington Meet (braised lamb kidneys in port wine sauce), steak au poivre, savoury mushrooms with coriander, tomato & wine.*

16th century and of warm Cotswold stone, very little has changed here since Russell and Tina with Stephen and Alison Gainford took over. The staff were retained, including the chef, whose style is good quality traditional English and established continental favourites. Children are welcomed, spoiled even, with a large beer garden, stream with fish ponds, play area and aviary. Oxford, Cheltenham, Gloucester and Bath are within easy driving and Shakespeare's Stratford beckons. A relaxed and pleasant place, with inglenooks and beamed ceilings and in character with this charming village.

THE KING'S ARMS

Market Square, Stow-on-the-Wold.   Tel. (0451) 30364

Location:	Market Square.
Credit cards:	Access, Visa, Amex.
Accommodation:	5 doubles, 3 family, 2 twins.
Beers:	Bass, Worthington, Toby.
Lagers:	Tennents, Carling. Plus draught cider.

Examples of bar meals (lunch & evening, 7 days): *steak & mushroom pie, cottage pie, plaice, scampi, hot mackerel in cheese sauce, ploughman's, sandwiches, blackboard specials eg liver & bacon & sausage casserole, garlic prawns & mushrooms served with cheese on garlic bread, quiche, homemade fruit pies & trifles.*
Examples of restaurant meals (evenings only, 7 days): *prawn & melon cocktail; steaks, mixed grill, local trout, half Cotswold chicken with chasseur sauce (or with chipolata, stuffing & cranberry sauce), lamb cutlets. Sweet trolley.*

Alf Glazebrook and Sandra Marshall took over here only in December '89, but have already earned a reputation for the quality of their food, with stress on freshness and cooking to order. They inherit a distinguished history; licensed in 1548, no less a person than King Charles I lodged here in 1645 (royal coat of arms over the door), and the Earl of Warwick in 1708 took refreshment, but we lesser mortals are also sure of a welcome and attentive service. The main ground floor bar, with exposed beams and open fires, is typical of its era. Upstairs is the restaurant, residents' lounge and bedrooms, all recently refurbished. Live entertainment planned. Well behaved children welcome. Car park.

THE QUEEN'S HEAD

Market Square, Stow-on-the-Wold.   Tel. (0451) 30563
        Location: Town centre.
    Credit cards: Not accepted.
           Beers: Donningtons (based in Stow).
           Lagers: Carlsberg, Carlsberg Export.

Examples of bar meals (lunch & evening Mon - Sat. Snacks only Sun lunch): *homemade lasagne, liver & bacon casserole, game pie, steak & kidney pie, fish pie, chicken & mushroom pie, cheese & brocolli flan, chilli, dbl Glocs ploughman's. Toffee pudding (speciality).*

The last battle of the Civil War was fought nearby, in the early 1600s. Who knows, perhaps some of the adversaries called here to acquire Dutch courage, for the pub did exist then. Were they to meet now for a pint and game of darts, they would surely be pleased to see how little it has changed, if in a rather friendlier atmosphere! They might even recognise some of the classical music playing softly in the background. Landlord Timothy Eager is understandably proud of Sporting Life's description of his as the 'best pub in The Cotswolds' (it's close to Cheltenham racecourse). Both bars are full of character, and in either you can partake of good traditional 'farmhouse' cooking, and take the chance to try the local brew - Donningtons have only 15 outlets. Children welcome. Small patio. Parking in square.

CHERINGTON ARMS

Cherington, nr Shipston-on-Stour.   Tel. (0608 75) 233
> Location: Lower end of village, 2 miles off A34.
> Credit cards: Not accepted.
> Beers: Flowers IPA, OB. Guinness.
> Lagers: Stella Artois, Heineken.

Examples of bar meals (lunchtime 7 days, evenings except Sat.): *trout grilled in butter, golden scampi, chicken Kiev, quiche Lorraine, sausage & egg, homemade steak & kidney pie, chilli, curry, lasagne, ploughman's.*
Examples of restaurant meals (lunch & evening, 7 days): *pork sate with barbecue sauce, gingered beef casserole, seafood platter, steaks. American lemon gateau, raspberry & redcurrant pie, icecream specials. Trad. Sun. lunch.*

Immerse yourself in tranquility here in lovely surrounds; the large gardens back on to the river, so stretch out and watch the wildfowl amble past. Just over the county border, the pub itself is an attractive old building, retaining its period charm. The dining room and lounge extension are carefully sympathetic to the original character, with exposed beams etc. Richard and Wendy Cox offer quite comprehensive menus, further supplemented by a separate children's section, icecream specials (treat yourself to a 'Cherington Glory'), and vegetarians are not forgotten. Parties up to 40 can be catered for in the dining room (special menus by request). Booking preferred for Sunday lunch. Large car park.

THE FALCON

Watery Lane, Wooburn Moor, nr High Wycombe.   Tel. (062 85) 22752

Location:	Off A40 at garage between Beaconsfield and Loudwater.
Credit cards:	Not accepted.
Beers:	Wethereds, Flowers, Boddingtons, Marstons, Brakspears, Castle Eden (beers vary).
Lagers:	Stella Artois, Heineken.

Examples of bar meals (11:30 - 2:30pm, 7 days): *steak & kidney pie, Cornish pastie, chilli, chicken or beef curry, salads, Buckingham pie, ploughman's, sandwiches, daily specials.*

22 years running the same pub is quite an achievement these days. Robin and Marjorie Beckley have naturally long established a loyal local following, and much banter is exchanged over the bar, but they are nevertheless pleased to welcome newcomers and put them at their ease. The one 17th century bar lends itself to cosy comfort and relaxation. The low beams and open fires are particularly inviting on a cold winter's night, and generous helpings of good food provide inner warmth. Special mention must be made of the garden; beautifully kept, and shaded by mature trees, it is an idyllic spot to sup with a pint on a warm summer's day. Children very welcome – small public play park adjacent. Good parking.

THE WALNUT TREE

Fawley, nr Henley-on-Thames.   Tel. (0491) 63360/617

Location:	East end of village (best approach from A4155).
Credit cards:	Access, Visa.
Accommodation:	3 doubles (2 en suite).
Beers:	Brakspears.
Lagers:	Stella Artois.

Examples of bar meals (lunch & evening, 7 days): *deep-fried camembert with gooseberry dip, chicken Kiev with salad, fillet steak au poivre, fillet of beef stroganoff, salads, vegetarian.*
Examples of restaurant meals (Thurs. - Sat. evenings): *whole prawns sauteed in ginger & garlic, roast duckling with cherries & kirsch, braised stuffed sirloin of beef, chicken breast stuffed with prawns, Dover sole. Trad. Sun. lunch.*

Just inside Bucks, The Walnut Tree is tucked away in this lovely corner of The Chilterns, near to the beautiful Hambleden and Turville valleys. It is worth seeking out, for Geoffrey and Diana Knight proffer not only a genuine welcome, but rather imaginative homecooked food, as a glance at the examples above will suggest, and served in generous amounts. One may eat in either of the two comfortable bars, the outside covered patio, or the quite stylish 50-seater restaurant. There's also a pleasant grassed area at the front, with rustic tables and chairs under the shade of trees. Children welcome. Good parking.

THE KINGS ARMS

Skirmett, nr Henley-on-Thames.   Tel. (049 163) 247

Location:	Village centre.
Credit cards:	Access, Visa, Amex.
Accommodation:	5 doubles (2 en suite).
Beers:	Brakspears, Flowers, Ruddles, guest.
Lagers:	Stella Artois, Carlsberg, Heineken.

Examples of bar meals (lunch & evenings): *spare ribs, deep-fried pate filled mushrooms, 16ozs rump steak, tandoori chicken, filled jacket potatoes, ploughman's.* Examples of restaurant meals (as above): *goujons of sole musat, fillet steak Rossini, chicken supreme saute Provencale, Hambleden Valley hat pie (venison, game & bacon in wine sauce).*

What sets this apart from most other inns? Cuisine would have to be high on the list. The menu is varied and interesting, whether in the bar or candlelit restaurant, and all is freshly prepared. Try the local 'Chiltern Valley' wine - it might surprise you! Friendly hosts James and Jennifer Byrne extend a special welcome to visitors, and if staying overnight you are guaranteed a superb view over the beautiful Hambledon Valley; the 400-years-old inn stands right in the heart of it, surrounded by wooded slopes. Inside is also easy on the eye, nicely furnished and with beamed ceilings and large inglenook fireplace. The Turville room is ideal for business meetings, wedding receptions etc. Children welcome, and garden with swings.

THE ROSE & THISTLE

6 Station Road, Haddenham.   Tel. (0844) 291451
Location: 200 yds from church and village pond.
Credit cards: Access, Visa, Diners.
Accommodation: One twin, one double.
Beers: Greene King.
Lagers: Harp, Kronenbourg.

Examples of bar & restaurant meals (lunchtime 7 days, evenings Tues. - Sun., except Sundays in winter): *steaks, duck, chicken, gammon, fish platter, plaice, scampi, beef & kidney pie, chilli, pizzas, steakburgers, ploughman's, sandwiches. Range of sweets.*

England's largest village (pop. 6,500) is also distinguished by this splendid family pub, complete with large walled garden. The giant boot and slide are unfortunately for children only, but inside the grown-ups will appreciate that special appeal of a 300-years-old building, winsome and full of character. The separate restaurant is a converted barn, also available for parties, functions and business meetings. There are two bars, and Brian and Sue Wells maintain a high standard for food and service, at most affordable prices. Small car park, but unrestricted parking on road. As we go to press, the pub is being taken over by Greene King as part of an expansion programme, but will remain under Brian and Sue's management.

Buckinghamshire

THE BLUE FLAG

Cadmore End, nr High Wycombe.   Tel. (0494) 881183
Location: On B482 Marlow to Stokenchurch road.
Credit cards: Access, Visa, Diners, Amex.
Accommodation: 16 doubles/twins, all en suite.
Beers: Theakstons, Wadworth, Adnams, Websters, Morlands.
Lagers: Stella Artois, Carlsberg.

Examples of bar meals (lunch & evening, 7 days): *fresh or smoked salmon, barbecued pork ribs, lamb steaks in mint honey, lobster & game in season.*
Examples of restaurant meals (lunchtime except Sat., and every evening.): *potted crab & mushrooms, parma ham with melon, scampi stir fry in oyster sauce, whole Dover sole, roast duckling, grilled peppered sirloin, escalope of veal in cream & brandy. Vegetarian dishes & salads. Sweets & liqueur coffees.*

This freehouse on the eastern edge of beautiful Hambleden Valley has undergone a remarkable transformation, with the addition of a new wing of 16 bedrooms. Proprietor Ken Chevis is a master chef, so no surprise that discerning customers travel from all over The Chilterns to dine in the 50 seater regency style restaurant (children welcome). Impeccably furnished, it has a fine inglenook, beamed ceiling, velvet back chairs and chandeliers. For less formal dining, the bar is also very pleasing, with oak timbers adorned with brass, and an excellent selection of good ales. With wife Vicki, Ken has blended the old and new perfectly to create a most commendable country inn. Ample parking.

100

THE PHEASANT INN

Windmill Street, Brill.   Tel. (0844) 237104

Location: Just off A4011 north of Thame.
Credit cards: Not accepted.
Beers: Burton, guests.
Lagers: Skol, Castlemaine XXXX.

Examples of bar meals (lunch & evening, 7 days): *homemade soups, homemade lasagne, spare ribs & barbecue sauce, asparagus pancake, brillburger, seafood platter, chilli, ham'n'eggs, blackboard specials.*
Examples of restaurant meals (available as above): *rainbow trout with prawns or cashew nuts, scampi masquerade (in mild curry sauce flav. with Malibu, served with coconut, pineapple, rice & side salad), steaks, chicken cornucopia (breast in cream & mushroom sauce in puff pastry horn). Cheesecake, hot black cherries, peaches & cream in puff pastry horn.*

Boasting the best view in Buckinghamshire, over seven counties, The Pheasant is pleasantly situated next to a 300 years old windmill. Children can play around the mill in safety, allowing their parents to relax in the large garden. It enjoys an excellent reputation for good food, especially for steaks and the famous 'Brillburger': locally made pure beefburger, topped with melted cheese, lettuce, mayonnaise, tomato and chilli relish, served in a bap with chips - all at just £2.95. The atmosphere is delightfully 'olde worlde', with a log fire providing winter cheer. Car parking is no problem - there are no yellow lines in Brill!

CHANDOS ARMS

83 Bicester Road, Long Crendon.   Tel. (0844) 208659
          Location: On B4011.
       Credit cards: Not accepted.
    Accommodation: B & B arranged opposite, on request.
             Beers: Wethereds, S.P.A., Flowers Keg & Original.

Examples of bar meals (12 - 2pm, 6 days. 7 - 8:45pm, Tues - Sat. No food on Sundays): *steak & kidney pie, chicken curry, large baps, ploughmans, salads. Blackboard specials eg lamb hotpot, duck & apricot pie.*
Examples of restaurant meals (available as above): *steaks, gammon, fresh trout, blackboard specials eg oxtail stew, vegetable bake, liver & bacon casserole. Spotted dick, treacle pudding.*

Nearly 400 years old, The Chandos Arms nestles at the Lower End of Long Crendon. The village is a treasure of medieval origin, with an abundance of thatched cottages and farmhouses. A lovely inglenook fire warms the cosy beamed bar. Leading from here is the Buttery bar, which serves as the main dining area. Hosts Barbara and Bryan Davies-Law extend a warm and friendly welcome to all - to enjoy pleasant conversation and sociabilty without the intrusion of gaming machines or juke box. Bryan does the evening cooking, and specialises in succulent gammons, steaks etc, and diet-wrecking puds! Dine al fresco in the pretty garden - children are welcome here and in the dining area, but early arrival is advisable in summer!

THE FOX INN

Buckingham Road, Edgcott, Aylesbury.   Tel. (0296 77) 338

Location:	2 miles off A41 Aylesbury/Bicester road.
Credit cards:	Not accepted.
Beers:	Chas. Wells, Adnams.
Lagers:	Red Stripe, Kellerbrau, Talisman LA.

Examples of bar meals (lunch & evening, 7 days): *burgers, scampi, gammon steak, ploughman's, jacket potatoes, sandwiches, salads.*
Examples of restaurant meals (7 - 9:30pm, 7 days): *prawn & pineapple served on poppadom smothered in seafood sauce, fresh mushrooms sautees in garlic butter & served in light sherry sauce; wide range of steaks, chicken with stilton, plaice with prawns & mushrooms, half roast duckling with rich orange sauce, vegetarian platter.*

Originally two cottages, The Fox served its first pint in 1920. 70 years later the best traditions of fine ales and good food are still observed, in the relaxed atmosphere of a friendly village local, under the personal supervision of congenial hosts Terry and Jenny Bailey. The focal point of village social life, the pub hosts weekly ladies and gents darts nights, dominoes and weekly quiz night, but visitors need not feel like strangers. The intimate candlelit restaurant enjoys widespread repute, popular as a romantic setting for dinner. Children are also welcome, and there's a large beer garden. Ample parking.

THE CROOKED BILLET

Bicester Road, Ham Green, Kingswood, Aylesbury.   Tel. (0296) 77239

Location: A41 Bicester/Aylesbury road.
Credit cards: Access, Visa, Diners, Amex.
Beers: Wadworth 6X, Tetley, Burton.
Lagers: Lowenbrau, Skol, Swan Lite.

Examples of bar meals (12 - 3pm, 7 - 10pm, 7 days): *steaks, ploughman's, jacket potatoes with various fillings, salads.*
Examples of restaurant meals (as above): *smoked mackerel mousse, garlic mushrooms, homemade pate; halibut Florentine (stuffed with spinach, coated with sauce of brandy, cream & butter), aubergine en croute, steaks, escalopes of veal in ginger wine, beef stroganoff, chicken stuffed with prawns (poached and served on crouton with brandy, white wine & cream sauce). Business Persons lunch. Trad. Sun. roasts.*

Under new family management (Mr Fosh is a master cellarman), this 16th century coaching inn, which had been shamefully run-down, re-opened in May '90 after total refurbishment and improvement. The old beams were revealed, fireplaces rediscovered, a genuine Victorian mirror mounted behind the bar, and banquette seating arranged for greater intimacy. A 30 seater restaurant was created, and the old coach house converted to a splendid function room with dance floor, capable of seating 100. It's all carpeted throughout, and the results are most impressive. The vastly improved menu is now one of the most comprehensive in the area. Children are very welcome, and have a play area in the large garden. Bar billiards and skittles. Ample parking.

THE PHOENIX INN

11 Queen Catherine Road, Steeple Claydon.   Tel. (0296) 738919
      Location: Close to Claydon House.
  Credit cards: Not accepted.
        Beers: ABC, Tetley, Wadworth 6X.
       Lagers: Skol, Carlsberg Export.

Examples of bar meals (lunch 7 days, evenings except Sunday): homemade steak pies, steak & stilton pie, steak & kidney pie, shepherds pie, chilli, chicken Kiev, jacket potatoes, ploughman's, sandwiches. Sunday roasts (should be booked before Friday evening).

A very cheerful pub, this, with an air of good humour and chatty, helpful staff. It sits comfortably in its rural village surrounds, a rather pretty 16th century thatched inn close to the National Trust's Claydon House. Good old traditional pub pastimes are pursued; cribbage, darts and pool, as well as a regular 'yard of ale' contest - the record is currently held by a lady, to the chagrin of egotistical males! Food is well above average, excellent homemade pies being the speciality. There's a family room and garden with play area, and Alison and Paul Underwood (and probably their regulars) will make you feel welcome.

THE SWAN INN

Winslow Road, Gt Horwood.   Tel. (0296) 712556
          Location: Village centre.
       Credit cards: Not accepted.
    Accommodation: Available at Grange opposite.
            Beers: Ruddles, Websters, Guinness.
           Lagers: Fosters, Carlsberg, Holsten Export.

Examples of bar meals (lunch & evening, Wed - Sat): *chicken curry, deep fried cod, vegetable lasagne, blackboard specials eg homemade steak & kidney pie, chilli & garlic bread, seafood platter, kebabs, 4 vegetarian.*
Example of restaurant meals (evenings only, Thurs - Sat, other nights by arrangement): *14" mixed grill, chicken chasseur, Dover sole, steaks, duckling a l'orange, trout with celery & walnut stuffing. Gateaux, deep pan apple pie.*

Gt Horwood has been dealt with kindly by the passing centuries, exemplified best by the 12th century church and the 17th century Swan. Once a coaching inn, it is not without the prerequisite ghost, in the form of 'Arthur' who, fully liveried, allegedly frequents the lounge. Perhaps he likes to warm himself on the pine logs in the inglenook (the restaurant has one, too), and customers are welcome to roast their nuts. The warmth of the welcome is provided by John and Sheila Parry of three years occupancy. Children and hearty eaters are welcome in the restaurant, where the mixed grill is of gargantuan proportions, and Sheila's home cooking has achieved note in leading guides. Pool and darts, beer garden. Car parking.

ROBIN HOOD INN

Brackley Road, Buckingham.   Tel. (0280) 813387

Location:	A422, 3-4 miles south of Silverstone.
Credit cards:	Not accepted.
Beers:	Wadworth 6X, Hook Norton, Varsity, Morlands, 3 guests, Beamish, Guinness.
Lagers:	Bitburger, Marston Pilsner, Tuborg, plus handpump cider.

Examples from menu (available lunch Mon-Sat, evening Wed-Sat): *Hawaiin pasta with cashew nuts, fennel a l'Italian, mandarin duck with Drambuie, venison with port & mushrooms, vegan curry, sweet & sour Cantonese chicken, Somerset casserole, local ham & beef, salads & vegetarian meals a speciality, varied seasonally.*

There has been an inn or refreshment post on this site for around 250 years, here in a hamlet with the unusual name of Bufflers Holt. There are many local tales of the origin of the name; some say it derives from the Duke of Buckingham's herd of buffalo, others that 'bufflers' is a 17th century slang word for drovers. Rural connections are maintained by rustic furnishings and paintings by local artists. In summer, the pub is surrounded by beautiful flowering baskets, and vegetables are grown for the kitchen by a local market gardener on proprietor Ralph and Marlene's paddocks. No less than 36 whiskys and 14 homemade wines (including parsnip, cowslip and birch) are stocked, and they were runners-up in Addlestone's cellarman of the year 1989. Just one mile from lovely Stowe School gardens (National Trust).

THE QUEENS HEAD

Main St., Chackmore, nr. Buckingham.   Tel: (0280) 813004

Location:	Just off Buckingham to Silverstone road.
Credit cards:	Not accepted.
Beers:	A.B.C., Bass, Wadworth 6X, Guest.
Lagers:	Skol, Castlemaine.

Examples from menu: (lunch daily, and every evening except Mondays): *Steaks, homemade pies, chillies, lasagne, extra large ploughmans, treacle pudding, spotted Dick, chocolate pudding.*

A great place for car enthusiasts! Being very close to Silverstone, the Queens Head often has a fascinating array of vintage cars parked outside during the vintage clubsmens meeting weeks. Also, catch the Silverstone racing teams there, having a pint during the Grand Prix season. A nice, traditional English pub, with good old satisfying English food. An old, beamed, listed building with open fires in winter and a separate dining area. A safe, sheltered, totally enclosed garden, is ideal for the kiddies. Swings too! Nearest to Stowe School National Trust gardens.

INDEX

Berkshire

*denotes accommodation

Buckinghamshire

Gloucestershire

*denotes accommodation

Oxfordshire

* denotes accommodation

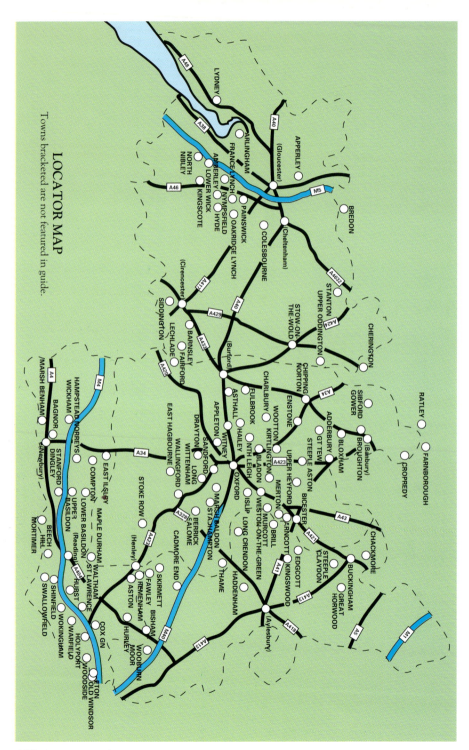

LOCATOR MAP

Towns bracketed are not featured in guide.

112